The

Structure

of

Human Decisions

DAVID W. MILLER

Professor
Columbia University

MARTIN K. STARR

Professor
Columbia University

THE
STRUCTURE
OF
HUMAN DECISIONS

Prentice-Hall, Inc., *Englewood Cliffs, New Jersey*

Printed in the United States of America

Library of Congress Catalog Card Number: 67-24023

Current printing (last digit):

18   17   16   15   14   13   12

PRENTICE-HALL INTERNATIONAL, INC., *London*
PRENTICE-HALL OF AUSTRALIA, PTY. LTD., *Sydney*
PRENTICE-HALL OF CANADA, LTD., *Toronto*
PRENTICE-HALL OF INDIA PRIVATE LTD., *New Delhi*
PRENTICE-HALL OF JAPAN, INC., *Tokyo*

To my daughter
RACHEL MILLER

To my sons
CHRISTOPHER AND LOREN STARR

Preface

This book examines the structure of decision problems from the viewpoint of an integrated theory of decisions. Within this framework, a logical, rational approach is blended together with scientific methodology. Using only the most elementary mathematics, the reader learns:

1. How to recognize the appropriate classification for a decision problem, and
2. How to approach problems of each class in accord with the present theory.

The classification of decision problems that we establish is pragmatically satisfying and theoretically significant. It enables a manager or an administrator to visualize his activities in a new way. Using this logic, quite complex decision problems can be resolved. Certainly, there are times when the assistance of a specialist may be warranted—for both problem formulation and the evaluation of results. However, the nonspecialist can always obtain guidance and enlightenment by referring to the decision theoretic structure.

With this in mind, we have given the reader an overview of as many relevant aspects of decisions as we possibly could. As a result, he comes away from this book with the realization that decision theory is broadly powerful and highly evolved. He discovers (with some surprise) that although the relevant principles of decision theory are logical and scientific it is not necessary to use anything but the simplest mathematics to explain them.

Decision-making is a root process. It is intertwined with all human activity. These roots are so fundamental to process and accomplishment that they take on a vital organic meaning without reference to the "real" detail of any particular problem. That is why this book could be written. Few who have not dwelt deliberately and at length on the nature of deciding are aware of how sensibly and straightforwardly decisions lend themselves to theoretical formulation. With a few strong principles we can organize the critical decision elements into basic sets that repeat themselves over and over again in every problem.

Many new methodologies, called by such various names as operations research, management science, and cybernetics are concerned with the decision process. We view these new arrivals to the decision-making scene as* totally expected aspects of the evolving interest in applied decision theory. This positive viewpoint is confirmed at every turn. The reader will observe that frequent reference is made to these new methods. Without them many decision problems cannot be formulated and even more of them cannot be resolved.

But, we do not elaborate in this book on the specific techniques of operations research, cybernetics, and other new methodologies. The reader who wishes to pursue such goals must turn elsewhere to study the structure and nature of decision-assisting *tools*. Still, having read this book, he can avoid being trapped with thinking that the new methodologies are simply explained by a new set of tools. We emphatically reject the approach which identifies operations research, management science, and cybernetics with a heterogeneous assortment of mathematical tools. In our conception of them, these fields are a continuum of *methods embedded in concepts*. They are based on philosophies and principles that underlie model-building and model-use and not just the means to manipulate data within the decision theory framework. This continuum of methods reflects the widest spectrum. It begins with useful but crude qualitative models and reaches to the most highly refined forms of mathematical expression.

The idea for this book arose from the excellent reception accorded to our text, *Executive Decisions and Operations Research* since its first printing in 1960. It was pointed out to us (often) that these ideas about decisions which make sense when applied in a business context could be directly generalized to apply to all decision-making activities. Words like executive, manager and administrator are more than terms associated with business. We recognize their complete functional parallel in any organization no matter whether its primary goals are those of business, government or other institutions. Accordingly, *The Structure of Human Decisions* has been designed to apply wherever man commits himself to a rational decision process.

DAVID W. MILLER

MARTIN K. STARR

Contents

x

The

Structure

of

Human Decisions

PART I

ORGANIZATIONS
AND
DECISIONS

1

Science
and
Administration

Management, as defined by *Webster's New International Dictionary*, is the "judicious use of means to accomplish an end." This definition may be too broad for our purposes, but not drastically so. Granted, we don't think that managing personal and family affairs is comparable with managing corporations, institutions, and other large organizations. Recently, however, there has been less and less reluctance to acknowledge that governments, hospitals, and libraries require a management team. This extension of the management concept can be traced to a growing awareness of the fundamental similarities in the basic patterns of all administrative issues.

Let us consider the management of business. At once, we think of business as *we* know it—business in our terms and in our style. But consider the Dobuan Islander of the South Pacific who speculates in shell necklaces from the southern islands and arm-shells from the northern islands. Using *wabuwabu* (which is the name given to the strategy of a good businessman) the Dobuan accumulates his fortune while maintaining the movement of shell necklaces in a clockwise direction and arm-shells in a counter-clockwise direction through the Kula ring of islands. A modern executive whose experience is limited to his own kind of management culture would feel like a fish out of water if he tried to negotiate on Dobuan terms. Similarly, in Burma when the accumulation of capital was not an overriding objective of business, and the pleasure of bargaining was even more important than the achievement of profit, we would have found the term "business management" awkward to apply. Yet, even in such unusual cases, some basic and transferable patterns have come to be recognized. The tools of economists can be employed and the knowledge of social scientists can increase our understanding. The culture rules are different but an important core of fundamentals transcends these rules.

The same reasoning applies to managements concerned with other objectives than those of business. Public administration as well as military and institutional management are as dependent upon sensible decision structures as are business, industry, and commerce. Transferability of the management function among the widest array of organizational contexts is now widely accepted. We have merely to note the number of individuals who have crossed successfully from one type of organization to another to confirm empirically what our logic indicates.

We shall avoid restricting our concept of management to any one type of organization. Similarly, we shall have no need to limit our considerations only to those ends which are customary in our own business, governmental, and institutional practices. We do not wish to cultivate an overly narrow concept of management, which could, in turn, produce a restricted view of the decision function. Such narrowness arises whenever we allow the ends to eclipse the means.

CHANGING CONCEPTS OF MANAGEMENT

The emphasis on traditional ends or goals has imposed a veil hindering the search for those elements of management which are transferable to any management or administrative situation. Business has evolved in this environment and a great deal of business-school training has reinforced this tendency by concentrating on special situations, specific techniques, and the propagation of customs, traditions, and attitudes.

An analysis of the evolution of management thinking shows, however, that two currents run side by side. One line of development emphasizes the necessity of mastering administrative methods as they exist at any given time. The other is devoted to the determination of those elements that are common to all management situations. Progress in the latter direction has been consistent and significant for many years. Our modern manager is, in fact, better equipped to tackle Dobuan or Burmese business practices than he suspects.

This characteristic universality of management exists because certain elements and patterns can be learned and utilized independently of the specific area of application. We are now aware that managing a retail shoe store has much in common with managing an oil refinery, a library, or a hospital. The same applies to manufacturing radios or running an airline. Implicit in this notion is the ability to assess managerial efficiency on a cross-industry and cross-institutional basis; although more demanding, the same can be said for cross-cultural systems. Much work remains to be done before it will be possible to compare the managerial efficiency of a large computer firm with that of a small factory in the Congo producing wood carvings.[1] Within reason, however, a transferable science of management systems can be said to exist.

Decision theory in conjunction with operations research and management science are the present-day culmination of this aspect of management's evolution. At the moment they are the most advanced developments available for generalizing among administrative situations. At a describable level they are equally applicable to Dobu, Burma, Afghanistan, the Congo, and the United States of America.

Operations research (O.R.) has been purposely developed by and for management. Military management in Great Britain was the first to use O.R. *consciously*—one of many developments that have appeared in wartime when the urgency of the situation accelerated normal rates of progress. Today military managements all over the world use O.R. The same is true of business organizations and other institutions in the worldwide sense.

SCIENTIFIC MANAGEMENT

The manager is our prototype of the decision-maker. Call this decision-maker whatever you will (executive, administrator, team coach, captain, president, chairman, general, or head of the family), he is an individual with decision responsibilities. No matter what name *you* give him, he is the same central figure in *our* context.

Business has made more of a sustained fuss about the manager's role than any other organizational system. Both in practice and in training it has made major contributions toward furthering the understanding of the decision responsibility of administrators. Examining history we find that formal training programs not connected with apprenticeship appeared as early as 1478.[2] A book on arithmetic for busi-

---

[1] See some of the attempts in this direction made by Barry Richman and Richard Farmer in *Comparative Management and Economic Development* (Homewood, Ill.: Richard D. Irwin Inc., 1965).

[2] Before that, as early as Babylonian times, the institutions for business education were in the household or small merchants' shops.

ness was printed at Treviso, Italy, in the fifteenth century. At the end of the seventeenth century Jacques Savary wrote *Le parfait negociant; ou Instruction generale pour ce qui regarde le commerce de tout sorte de marchandises.* This book, apparently well received, was reprinted several times. In England, William Scott wrote an *Essay of drapery, or The compleate citizen, trading justly, pleasingly, profitably.* At about the same time Jan Impyn completed the first Dutch book on accounting. His instructions were that the accounting journal should begin with the prayer, "May God our merciful Saviour vouchsafe me grace to make a profit and preserve me from all bad fortune."

These early works were important for the interest that they generated and because they led to a practice of searching and self-questioning, which management has not yet completed. Some of the earliest questioning can be traced to Thomas Watts, who conducted a school on Abchurch Lane in London. Watts called for the development of principles and the comparison of principles with practice. In Watts' *An Essay on the Proper Method of Forming the Man of Business* (1716), we find the interplay of generalization with specific prescription. Watts emphasized arithmetic, accounting, mathematics (including algebra and geometry), and mensuration. The last point is particularly interesting because it seems to have been forgotten after Watts' time. Not until the early part of the twentieth century did management reawaken to the problems and importance of measurement theory. The reawakening has been gradual, and we cannot help but wonder if a session or two in Thomas Watts' class on mensuration would not prove helpful to all of us. Watts' stress on principle, generalizations, and mathematics is the progenitor of decision theory and operations research in our present day. To quote from Watts:

> The several parts of the Mathematicks are of that extensive Use and Benefit to Mankind, that hardly anything is to be done without them; Consequently, the Man of Business can have no small Share in these Sciences: For he that has a thorough Knowledge in them, must have the best Foundation laid, and a Mind exquisitely furnish'd for the undertaking of any Business.

Management is always looking for better ways to do things. In the early 1900s Frederick W. Taylor concerned himself with the problems of production management and demonstrated that management could improve the means it used to accomplish ends. Some of his results were so startling that his methods swept across the United States. This movement, known as "scientific management," was later extended into time and motion studies and work-simplification methods. Taylor was responsible for the rebirth of interest in measurement. Undoubtedly, his work also played an important part in creating interest in management training.

The growth of schools of business, management, and administration, both in size and number, is fair evidence of organizational support and encouragement for management training and management research. If the importance of transferable methods and general procedure had not been recognized, it is doubtful that such schools would have grown to the preeminent position that they occupy today. Recent stress on executive training programs (so-called continuing education and retooling) provides additional dimensions by which to judge the extent of this interest. If the quality of an administrator were determined primarily by his knowledge of ritual, custom, and tradition, apprenticeship training would have been more attractive than formal school training.

INFORMATION FOR DECISIONS

Perhaps the most general characteristic of management problems is that some kinds of resources are always being used as inputs to produce some kind of outputs. These resources generally have alternative uses. Also a cost must be sustained in using the resource. Similarly, the output, or benefit, from using the resources generally has value. Efficient management may try to minimize the costs associated with a given benefit or to maximize the benefit associated with a given use of resources. These opportunities invariably generate management interest in some kind of cost-benefit analysis.[3]

This is why one of the first general methodologies management discovered was accounting, for accounting was neither limited to a specific industry nor restricted to a particular area of business. The history of modern accounting starts with a book by Pacioli, *Summa de arithmetica*, published in Italy in 1494, which contains a descriptive statement of double-entry bookkeeping methods. This approach did not originate with him since he refers to it as the Venetian system. It was 1543, a half-century later, when Hugh Oldcastle wrote the first descrip-

[3] It is important enough to deserve emphasis that one or the other or both of the sides of such an input-output analysis may not be measurable in dollars or in any obvious quantitative form. For a variety of interesting discussions of the resulting problems and ways to solve them see Robert Dorfman, ed., *Measuring Benefits of Government Investments* (Washington, D.C.: The Brookings Institution, 1965).

tion in English of the methods of bookkeeping. Thomas Watts refers
to this method of keeping accounts as his "darling science" and expresses contempt for those who kept single-entry books.

Interest in accounting methods grew rapidly in the nineteenth century. James Bennett of New York wrote *The American System of Practical Bookkeeping* in 1824. Eighteen years later 19 editions had been
published. Bennett used his book as a text for classes that he conducted
for business students from his house at 97 John Street in New York
City. At about the same time, Thomas Jones founded the New York
Commercial Academy at 183 Broadway in New York City, and published his book *Principles and Practices of Bookkeeping.*

Our purpose in stressing accounting at this point is that accounting
was one of the first generalized methods developed by management. It
is significant as a pioneer quantitative method and as the first well-
structured information available for the resolution of decision problems. The importance of accounting to the administrative function was
so great that it tended to crystallize in definite forms, which could be
put to work on specific problems. However, accounting problems were
inextricably connected with problems of observation and measurement,
systems analysis, model construction, and decision theory. Certainly,
operations research is not an offshoot of accounting. But the forces
that brought accounting practices to the fore were not unlike the
forces that have introduced operations research to the world. We shall
have a great deal more to say about information for decisions in the
material that follows.

CHANGE IN OWNER-MANAGER RELATIONSHIP

Perhaps our discussion of management should have included some
phrase relating to the delegation of authority. The end of the nineteenth century and the beginning of the twentieth was the period of
enormous organizational expansion in the United States, which is
credited to the Captains of Industry. These Captains, with gigantic
reserves of personal vitality, directed their companies' fortunes in the
capacity of owner-managers, which was characteristic of smaller busi-
nesses. Gradually, as business began to move from its highly competitive, aggressive position to a more cooperative-competitive attitude, the
individual owner-manager began to disappear. In his place, an organizational structure evolved that had the capacity to delegate
authority for decisions and responsibility for the entire range of administrative tasks. Management had to learn how to cope with the

problems that large organizational structures produced. Personnel problems appeared as a result of the complex, hierarchical arrangements of organization. Social developments emphasized the uniqueness of labor, management, consumer, and stockholder. At the same time, legal involvements and governmental controls raised new problems, which the management team had to solve. The same structure evolved for military, governmental, and institutional systems.

DEVELOPMENT OF SPECIALISTS

Part of the answer was—and continues to be—specialization. The demands of organizational growth were incontestable. Specialization set the pattern for the traditional areas of management. Specialists were required for production, marketing, finance, personnel, real estate, business law, and so on. Then, within each of these areas, further specialization was required and as a result we had time standards, quality control, foundry methods, press shop operations, advertising, sales promotion, public relations, building codes, patent law, and the multitudinous remainder.

DEVELOPMENT OF GENERALISTS

Is an operations-research practitioner a specialist? Most certainly he is. However, he occupies the unique position of being a specialist in generalization. That is why the operations-research function is frequently located high up in the organizational structure.

The twentieth century has seen research and technological development spurt ahead with such impact that organizational identity could hardly be maintained. Faced with swift and startling developments, management has had to question whether it had an existence above and beyond the products it made or the services it offered. The answer was affirmative. A fundamental core of management know-how was indeed transferable. At the same time, the separation of owner and manager engendered an executive tradition which permitted management people to shift from one organization to another. Ultimately, management realized that it had an identity which was independent of any or all of the individuals who composed the management group.

The solution to modern management's problems was the development of the *executive-generalist*. Such administrators could maintain the company's existence no matter what product was made. They could develop abstract organizational forms which were independent of the individuals who at any time happened to compose the management group. They could coordinate the contributions of all of the specialists of an organization. Their task required the ability to employ structure before content in coping with the extreme diversity of information produced by the organization.

MANAGEMENT SCIENCE

Management recognized that the change in its role now required generalists. Individuals so trained could effectively operate in business, industry, city or federal government, hospitals, the armed forces, and schools, and could deal with behavioral scientists, research physicists, tax lawyers, and production foremen. To meet this challenge business schools have broadened their curriculums and have supported far-ranging research in management problems. More and more, independence from prescribed means and ends has been sought. Operations research and the decision-theory framework are part of a current, worldwide *management science* movement. They provide an important avenue for increasing the manager's ability to generalize and are a logical development in the evolutionary process of the managerial function.

Management science differs from Taylor's scientific management in many ways. It is not primarily concerned with production tasks and efficiency of men and machines. Rather, it views efficiency as a secondary achievement which should follow adequate planning. Both good and poor decisions can be implemented in an efficient way. A company can manufacture a high-quality product at minimum cost, but the product might not be the best choice for the company's objectives.

Management science is concerned with both short- and long-range planning. It attempts to establish whatever relationships exist between an organization's objectives and its resources. In this way, it cuts across the traditional areas of management. Such crossing of boundaries characterizes management science, which is *problem-oriented*. (See Chapter 7 for the discussion of what a "problem" is.)

Similarly, management science neither avoids nor overlooks the effects of behavioral problems, even though such problems cannot always be formulated or solved. Management science is essentially quantitative, although if important problems cannot be quantified they may be handled qualitatively. Whether quantitative or qualitative methods are applied, operations research is used to produce rational decisions and logical plans of action.

PROBLEMS

1. Mr. J, the President of E-Z Styles, Inc., objects when he learns that Mr. D, the chief designer, has hired management consultant Q to study the styling function. This relates to the way in which the full year's line of dresses is styled as well as to the style trends themselves. J states that the consultant Q has had no experience in the dress styling field, having previously worked for many years in the oil industry, as well as with the fabrication of metal parts.

   In response, Mr. D states that it is precisely this that allows Mr. Q to come to the problem with a fresh look. He also points out that Q was hired to look at the larger management problem, including sales and production methods, the company's inventory problem, and the overall purchasing function. Furthermore, he adds that the consultant has refused to undertake this job unless the styling function is included. Mr. D says that this very fact alone impresses him.

   Discuss the pros and cons of this argument between J and D.

2. The Homecraft Company manufactures a full line of work tools for the home. Over recent years it has obtained many foreign affiliates and has begun a program of moving its executives around from one place to another. What basis can you suggest to support this policy? What disadvantages might exist? How would you resolve these issues?

3. In what way might a thorough knowledge of management history have any bearing on an administrator's efficiency or effectiveness? Would his time be better spent learning something else?

4. What criteria, objectives, and abilities exist for a business school (a) in updating an experienced executive? (b) in teaching concepts of transferability to students with no previous work experience? (3) in determining how much specialization should temper generalization?

   What would be the likely long term result of emphasizing either generalization or specialization to the exclusion of the other?

5. Discuss: "Management had to question whether it had an existence above and beyond the products it made or the services it offered." To what extent do you think this is so?

6. Discuss: "Management realized that it had an identity which was independent of any or all of the individuals who composed the management group." To what extent do you think this is an accurate statement?

7. From the point of view of more or less transferability of the management function between different industries, how would you rate the following

familiar organizational areas: production, marketing, finance, accounting, personnel, and general management?

8. From the point of view of more or less transferability of the management function between different institutions, how would you rate the following: libraries, hospitals, museums, charities, civic governments, political parties, military systems, and postal operations?

9. Some believe that an increasing number of companies will find that the controller's function is ascending to the top corporate post. What do you think of this notion?

10. Why is it said that top organizational corporate posts now require a modern-day version of Renaissance man?

2 | Responsibility for Decisions

Theories of evolution are applicable to organizations as well as to species. Organizations cease to thrive when they find themselves unable to adapt to environmental and competitive changes. Unsuitable structures show up as marginal industries and unacceptable institutions, and eventually such organizations enter receivership where they either reorganize or cease to exist.

The ability of an organization to succeed in its environment and to adapt to change, or even to capitalize on change, is basically in the hands of management. In previous discussion it was pointed out that management's view of itself has not remained constant. Present-day management has redefined the administrative role to improve the organization's flexibility and responsiveness.

DECIDING AND DOING

The major function of the executive is improperly indicated by the strict derivation of the word. "Executive" derives from a Latin word meaning "to do," and the Oxford dictionary defines it in terms of "the action of carrying out or carrying into effect." Neither of these approaches would suggest that the main responsibility and function of the executive is to make decisions. Yet in modern business and industry this is precisely what is expected of him. He is rewarded and evaluated in terms of his success at making decisions. There is some incongruity in the term "manager," which we have already defined as a user of *judicious* means to accomplish an end. The emphasis is on doing, but judicious saves the day. The administrator is defined as one who directs the execution of the organization's affairs. This accents yet another organizational responsibility in keeping with society's expectations for management performance.

The typical manager has other functions in addition to making decisions. He has to *do* many other things. But most organizations make continual attempts to relieve the manager of his more or less routine operations so that he will have more time for the critical decision function. This conception of the executive does not diminish the importance of doing. Organizational structure is set up as the means for providing a great variety of services required by the organization, such as directing, coordinating, analyzing, and controlling. However, crucial questions of what, when, where, and how to do, are prior to the acts required for doing. These are the decision problems which must be dealt with. To the extent that management is involved in doing it will have less time to devote to deciding.

The distinction we are making between doing and deciding is certainly a drastic oversimplification. Such orderly and well-defined boundaries between functions do not exist. A decision initiates actions which in turn will generate the need for new decisions. The process is a never-ending one. The manager is necessarily immersed to some degree in both parts. Nonetheless, a conceptual separation of the two permits concentration on those aspects of the decision part of the process that can yield useful insights.

Although we concentrate on the decision side of the total process, we cannot afford to ignore interaction with the doing. If deciding and doing are strongly interrelated it can be misleading to separate them. This possibility must be considered before we can proceed to analyze the decision problem separately.

THE ORGANIZATION AS A COMMUNICATION NETWORK

In order to clarify the relationship between action and decision it will be useful to introduce a *model* of the organization, viewing it as a communication network. Throughout this book we shall be demonstrating the value of studying different models of organizations designed for different purposes.

A model can only be defined in terms of the purpose for which it is constructed. The model *abstracts the relevant aspects* of the organizational system and attempts to deduce how those aspects interact to produce effects related to our purpose. It must be emphasized that the only model which would be appropriate for all possible purposes is the organization itself. The reason for isolating or abstracting certain characteristics of an organization in the form of a model is to gain an understanding of the effect of the abstracted characteristics on the total organization. The risk involved in such abstractions is that other characteristics of the organization may be so important that ignoring them invalidates the model. However, even a valid model is at best a partial truth. Experience is the only final arbiter as to the successfulness of a specific model.

A communication network is a collection of points between which information is transmitted. Any telephone system provides a good example of a communication network. As a matter of fact, it was primarily problems of the sort that arise in connection with such communication networks as telephone systems that led to the development of a theory of these networks and the closely related information theory.

We can consider an organization as a communication network by ignoring all of its characteristics except those represented by the existence of information and its transmission between persons and places. Although this is a rather severe abstractive simplification of an organization, it is not as extreme as it might appear. The definition of "information" is not limited to standard forms of communication. Written memoranda and verbal exchanges are only one form of information. Blueprints, budgets, part numbers, and so on are other forms. Material and parts flowing through a factory or warehouse are also legitimate units of information. In fact, any characteristic of an operation that can be observed and recorded constitutes potential information for a communication network. The production of an item can be represented by the transmission of the information that that item has been added to inventory. The sale of an item can be transformed into the transmission of the information that that item has left inventory. At a later point, there can be the information transmission that a certain sum of money has been added to the organization's bank account. Similarly, other activities of the organization will have their information-flow analogs.

INPUT-OUTPUT AND THE BLACK BOX

One important distinction between the kinds of information that are transmitted arises from the fact that the organization is embedded in its environment. The outside world consists of suppliers, buyers, competitors, tax and regulatory agencies, and other groups. The information that comes into the organization from the outside world is *input*. In response to input the organization buys material and facilities, hires labor, prices its products, advertises, floats stock issues, and so fourth. These organizational responses are *outputs*.

It is useful at times to treat the organization as though it were covered by a black box and, therefore, completely unobservable. The "black box" is a convenient term to describe a system (organism or mechanism) whose structure is unknown—either because it cannot be observed or because it is too complex to be understood. (The notion of the black box has been borrowed by systems analysts from electrical engineers who used it to denote unspecified circuitry.) How well can the characteristics of the organization viewed as a black box be inferred from a knowledge of the inputs and outputs? Can reasonable predictions be made of the outputs that would occur for some hypothetical set of inputs if the properties of the black box cannot be inferred? The answers to both of these questions are a qualified "yes." The qualification depends upon the inherent structure of the information that appears in the inputs and outputs.

From a manager's point of view the black box does not apply to his organization, and he hardly likes to think that it covers his own behavior [see Figure 2.1(a)]. Instead, he thinks of the black box as covering the outside world [as in Figure 2.1(b)]. The output shown in Figure 2.1(a) is transformed into the input of Figure 2.1(b), where

FIGURE 2.1(a) Input-output model of the organization.

management controls the inputs. When the black box covered the organization, only the organizational output could be observed. This output was all doing and contained no deciding. In fact, deciding was

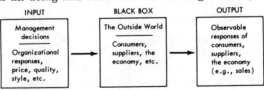

FIGURE 2.1(b) Input-output model of managerial control.

the circuitry that was hidden by the black box. By transforming to Figure 2.1(b), we have exposed the decision process and brought it into the realm of observable information.

From the standpoint of a communication network, a decision consists of instructions from one point in the network to other points. As a result of the decision these other points will process the information they receive in a different manner or will change the rate of flow of information passing through them. Or, of course, the decision may result in the establishment of new points in the communication network.

INFORMATION STORAGE AND MEMORY

A specific decision depends on the analysis, interpretation, and evaluation of information that is available to the decision-maker. Part of the information that comes to the manager is withdrawn from storage. Every organization has memory, or rather memories, in which data can be stored. The most obvious example of these memories are the organization's files. Other storehouses of organizational knowledge are the brains of the personnel that comprise the organization. The time required to obtain information stored in files can in some applications be prohibitively high. The brain is not reliable for information storage; memory is perhaps its weakest faculty. Computer memories have particular advantages in this respect but even the largest computers lack the flexibility and size that characterize cerebral storage of information.

It is quite apparent that the decision-maker can be deluged with information if he does not know how to select data that are pertinent to his problem. For this reason, information must be carefully categorized. Decision problems exist as to what information should be collected and in what form; where and how long it should be stored; when and by whom it should be called for; how it should be evaluated; when it should be updated, supplemented, and so on. Information models provide some help in answering these questions, which are essential for the *decision* activities of the manager. *Doing* would be collecting, recording, dispatching, and storing of information. It is quite clear that management prefers to minimize administrative time spent in this way.

INFORMATION FEEDBACK CHANNELS

A decision that has been made may be countermanded or supplemented by subsequent decisions. Any such change will, presumably, be based on additional information. This additional information can result from changes caused by the implementation of the decision or from sources that are extraneous to the implementation of the decision. To the degree that it is the former, the decision process is closely related to the doing. To the degree that it is the latter, the decision process is relatively independent of the doing.

To make this distinction clearer, we must add an additional element to the input-output model. The new factor is called a *feedback* channel. (This term is also derived from electrical engineering, where it is used to denote an electrical signal (output) that is fed back into the circuit from which it emanated.) Figure 2.2 illustrates two different feedback connections, labeled (IV) and (V).

Let us now examine the implications of the feedback links, assuming that the manager occupies the position of the black box. For our purposes, the black box is not so opaque as to entirely hide the operations of the executive. Feedback channel IV indicates the administrator's

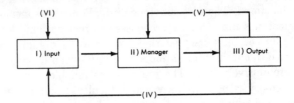

FIGURE 2.2 Input-output model of the organization with feedback channels.

ability to call for certain inputs and to specify the form in which these inputs should arrive. This matter was previously discussed in connection with memories and information storage. Basically, there are three types of inputs: (a) inputs that cannot be controlled, (b) inputs that are controlled by an outside agency with intelligence, and (c) inputs that an executive can control.

Link IV is the channel through which the administrator exercises whatever control he has over the inputs. In all cases there is a decision and an action to effectuate control. Whenever feedback channel IV operates, we see that doing and deciding are implicitly bound together in a sequence: DECIDE → DO → DECIDE → DO, and so on. The nature of organizational control requires that most outputs should be fed back for inspection, evaluation, and follow-up.

On the other hand, the manager responds to a great range of inputs that arrive via channel VI. These are the maneuvers of competitors, the changing situation of the economy, and a variety of factors that are essentially random events of importance to the company. Inputs that do not arrive via the feedback link pose a major challenge to executive decision-making ability; these inputs are examples of situations in which deciding and doing are separate. Great care must be exercised, however, in ascertaining that hidden feedbacks do not exist.

Feedback channel V is required to show that an administrative decision can produce an output capable of modifying the future behavior of the executive. That is, the executive can *decide to decide* in a certain way in the future. A decision can alter the attitudes and values of the decision-maker. In this case, the output does not affect inputs but symbolically achieves a rewiring of the not entirely opaque black box. The importance of *deciding how to decide* is not trivial. There are no pat solutions to this problem but there is methodology to help decision-makers. To the extent that the manager devotes his time and attention to channels V and VI, he is relegating the doing to other areas of the organization. When channel IV is operating, doing and deciding are bound together within the managerial province.

The input-output feedback model has helped to indicate the nature of the decision process and the limitations involved in separating it from other organizational processes. Let us consider a few practical examples of typical decisions in terms of the distinction between deciding and doing.

1. The lathe operator who decides to start his lathe will promptly reverse this decision if one of the cutting tools breaks. His decision is bound up with his doing.

2. The decision to build a new hospital, plant, or library might be countermanded because unforeseen difficulties in financing arise or because of unexpected changes in the overall situation. These factors are extraneous to the implementation of the decision, which therefore can legitimately be treated separately from the doing.

3. A decision to increase production might be revoked because of a sudden slump in sales, which is extraneous to the implementation. It might also be countermanded because of production-line difficulties that are directly tied to the implementation. Here the validity of separating deciding from doing depends on the point of view taken. In most organizations the decision-maker would be two different people, or at least it would be one man acting in the two different capacities of production and marketing management.

This last example suffices to show that no one model is adequate to describe and categorize all decisions. It also confirms that a considerable number of important decisions are sufficiently independent of the doing to permit them to be considered apart from their implementation.

CYBERNETIC SYSTEMS

When the input-output model with feedback links is fully developed we enter the domain of integrated control systems. Many controls can be automatic and self-monitoring. The study of control systems has been named *cybernetics*, and is a rapidly growing field of research.

The classic example of a feedback control system is the thermostat arrangement that regulates the temperature of many houses. The furnace produces heat that is measured by the thermostat, which, in turn, controls the furnace. In short, the thermostat feeds back to the furnace instructions based upon a comparison of the effect of the furnace's output with a criterion for the system's performance, i.e., the temperature setting. This idea of regulating the feedback signal in terms of deviations from the objectives of a system (or as an error measurement to correct the error) is at the heart of cybernetic theory. It is clear that the methodology of cybernetic systems can be applied to a variety of management functions which involve feedback.

Previously, we acknowledged that the inherent circularity of such feedback systems would make the separation of decisions from actions purely arbitrary. In other words, the deciding and the doing are too closely related to permit a valid distinction between them. However, the cybernetic model permits the separation of deciding and doing by calling for decisions which are made only once and which determine the *design* of the organizational process. It can be recognized that the inputs arriving via the feedback channel become *repetitive* and that many of these inputs call for repeat decisions which should not require executive time. Many organizational designs permit these feedback inputs to by-pass the manager and to pass instead across an assistant's desk or into an automated controller.

In Figure 2.3, the manager transmits decision criteria and operational requirements for the construction of an automatic decision-maker (or regulator). After that, he is relieved of the responsibility of employing the same decision criteria every time a given situation repeats itself. Of course, automatic decision-makers are seldom available except in specialized and highly instrumented process industries. Nevertheless, by transmitting decision instructions to subordinates in the form of policy and operating rules, the executive achieves almost the same degree of freedom.

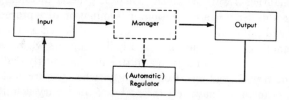

FIGURE 2.3 Automatic decision-making bypasses the manager but carries out his instructions.

In the case of the simple thermostat the basic decision criteria are:

1. The desired temperature gradients in the heated space.
2. The allowable fluctuations in temperature under conditions of steady demand, or sudden changes in demand (such as a door opening).
3. The location of the thermostat to deliver the required temperatures.
4. The cost of the installation.
5. The reliability of the error-sensing device.
6. The cost of maintaining the installation.
7. The element under control (fuel, heat valve, or whatever).

Thus we see that in spite of the relative simplicity of the thermostat example, many decisions must be made. Complex systems require many more decisions which, when treated in cybernetic terms, can be divorced from doing, even though they are based on feedback links that exist to control inputs. And it will be legitimate to treat decisions of this kind separately from their implementation.

Consideration of the different sorts of decisions made in business and other kinds of organizations indicates that decisions which are most clearly separate from their implementation are those made by persons who are high in the organizational hierarchy. This is in accord with the fact that most organizations make special efforts to formulate and communicate policy which can relieve their top executives of doing. A separate treatment of the decision process may, therefore, not be adequate for all decisions made within an organization, but it will certainly be relevant for many of the most important ones.

THE NATURE OF A DECISION

What are the properties of a decision? The word "decision" covers such a multitude of cases that it belongs to the class of omnibus words which semanticists warn us about. There is general dictionary agreement that a decision is a conclusion or termination of a process. However, the end point of one process can also be viewed as the starting point of another. This brings us into a hall of mirrors where each mirror reflects its image onto a facing mirror in a seemingly endless progression of transformations. Consequently, when we decide to decide . . . and so forth, we have left the realm of dictionary definition and have become entangled in a maze of reflective properties which defy analysis and interpretation. There are, of course, other words and phrases with similar properties, such as the will to will . . . , to try to try . . . , or think about thinking about thinking. This reflexive property of decisions is not illusory. The organizational question of what triggers decisions is another way of asking: What causes the manager to decide to decide? In addition to this complication, the class of functions called decisions is so broad and contains such great variety that the use of a simplified definition of decision can create confusion instead of adding intelligence.

Obviously, the manager has no monopoly on decisions. Everyone makes all kinds of decisions throughout his life. What school to attend, what profession to choose, what job to take, whom to marry, how to plan for retirement—these are some of the many crucial decisions which each person must make. It is precisely the ubiquity of the decision problem which has led so many persons in so many fields to attempt to analyze it. Philosophers, psychologists, economists, sociologists, logicians, and mathematicians have all attempted to deal with the decision problem.

What, then, is the decision problem? Simply the determination of how people should proceed in order to reach the best decisions. In other words, what methods can be used, what questions should be asked, what steps should be taken, what are best decisions, and so forth. Let us consider some conclusions of the many specialized thinkers who have studied the decision problem.

PHILOSOPHERS AND DECISIONS

Philosophers have concerned themselves mainly with the question of what constitutes a "good" decision, in fact, this is the major concern of ethics. Mostly they have dealt with the problem of the individual: How should I act so as to lead a good life? From this they have generalized to the question: What is a good life? Philosophers approach the problem in two ways: either by defining "good" and considering a variety of values as aspects of it, or by summing up acceptable values and considering the totality to represent "good." Many philosophers have conceived this "good" to have a kind of objective, real existence. Others have maintained that values are simply those things which a particular person wants to have and that, as such, they are subjective and cannot be established in concrete terms. In either case, the philosophers were dealing with a particular conception of the individual's decision problem—that of the free, untrammeled person who has chosen the values he wishes to achieve and who makes rational decisions in order to obtain his objectives.

Totally involved with questions of what is "good" is the issue of what accounts for what happens. Consequently, the philosophy of decisions has always been related to the "truth" of what is known (or believed) about the fundamental laws of the universe. Primitive man, driven by fear of the unknown, appointed moon and sun gods as the source of good and bad. Even as understanding of the material world increased, the implicit association of truth and goodness was taken to be self-evident, and both Socrates and Plato staunchly advocated their inseparable existence. Science began to probe further than the evident, but faith in the connection remained, so that in the nineteenth century great optimism prevailed that by the twentieth perfect decisions could be made because science would be able to explain the underlying truth of all phenomena. The nature of universal good was about to be discovered.

But with the birth of the twentieth century came a rash of contradictory evidence. The Heisenberg uncertainty principle coupled with the basic concepts of quantum mechanics reformulated truth as a probabilistic notion. By relating truth to risk and uncertainty, the fundamental connection between goodness and truth was shattered. Goodness remained a philosophical, theological, and personal matter. Individual truth came to be viewed as a property of cerebral-sensory systems; universal truth as approachable but ultimately unknowable. And so an operational philosophy of decisions developed, wherein the goodness of a decision would be measured by the extent to which its results satisfied the decision-maker's objectives.

ECONOMISTS AND DECISIONS

Typically, the values with which philosophy has dealt have been nonquantitative. How, for example, can happiness be quantified? Yet there is a range of human values that seems to be already quantified.

It contains all of the goods and services that are offered and purchased in the marketplace. That these things have value is apparent from the fact that people want them and are willing to sacrifice time and effort in order to get them. These values are conveniently, but imperfectly, quantified in terms of money.

The classical philosophers were cognizant of marketplace values, but relegated them to a subordinate position as compared to other kinds of values which they held constituted the "good." Adam Smith was trained in philosophy and one of his first works was on ethics. But despite his background in dealing with the higher values, it was one of his merits as an economist that he defined economics strictly in terms of the marketplace values. Smith believed that these economic values played a sufficiently important role in everyone's life to justify their scientific investigation. He also felt that such an investigation could only be successful if the higher, nonquantitative values were excluded from the province of economics.

The subsequent development of economics for a long time remained circumscribed within the limits established by Smith. The decision problems which economists have explored treat both sides of the supply-and-demand relationship. How much of a commodity will a producer make at a given price? How much of a commodity will a consumer buy at a given price? These and similar questions lead naturally to the prior question: What are the objectives of the consumer and the producer? The economists' answer has been framed in terms of the utility which the commodity will provide to the consumer and which the production of the commodity will give to the producer. (*Utility* is defined as the power to satisfy human wants.) The objective of the individual is held to be the maximization of the total utility he can achieve with his limited resources of time, effort, and money. The rationality of the individual is defined in terms of the utilization he makes of his scarce resources to achieve this end of maximization of utility. As we previously indicated, money is a convenient, but imperfect, measure of utility.

SOCIAL SCIENTIST AND DECISIONS

Contemporary developments in economics have emphasized the lack of realism of the assumption that individuals act so as to maximize their utility. There has not been an attack on the proposition that individuals should act so as to achieve a maximization of their utility. Rather, there has been sufficient evidence and supporting reasons to show that they do not act in this way. Among the reasons suggested have been the following: the inability of the individual to duplicate the rather recondite mathematics which economists have used to solve the problem of maximization of utility; the existence of other values (the higher values originally excluded by Smith) which, though not readily quantifiable, do cause divergences from the maximization of utility in the marketplace; the effect of habit; the influence of social emulation; the effect of social institutions. Many economists have been attempting to take these various factors into account in constructing economic theories, which they feel will show a closer correspondence to the real world.

By introducing such factors, economists have been trying to incorporate aspects of behavior into choice or decision situations. This has also been the concern of psychologists and sociologists. The work of psychologists would certainly tend to confirm the assertion that human beings have a variety of diverse motivations which do not lend themselves to maximization of utility—at least so long as utility is defined in terms of the *satisfactions* resulting from marketplace phenomena. Freudian theory is only one example of a conceptualization of human motivation that relegates rational calculations in decisions to a relatively minor role. Similarly, sociologists have accumulated considerable evidence to demonstrate the enormous influence of social institutions, habit, and tradition on the choices and decisions made by individuals. The effect of these psychological and sociological factors leads individuals to make decisions and to take actions without recourse to maximization of utility in the classical economic sense. Alternatively phrased, it can be said that these factors cause people to act irrationally—but it should be noted that this is simply a matter of definition, rationality having been defined as maximization of economic utility.

Thanks to the subjective definition of utility, it is possible for economists to maintain that all of these factors can be incorporated into economic theory. If, for example, an individual's market decisions are affected by his desire for dignity, then it can simply be said that he is maximizing utility and he ascribes a utility to dignity. The difficulty, however, remains. The utility an individual gains from a commodity or a service can be measured to some degree by observable market phenomena (e.g., how much of the commodity he will buy at different prices). But there is no convenient measuring unit for the utility of an intangible such as dignity. Therefore, even if these other factors can be theoretically expressed in terms of utility, the difficulties involved in

measuring the utilities prevent the theory from satisfactorily explain-
ing observed behavior and decisions.

LOGIC AND DECISIONS

Many different approaches to the decision problem converge on one
particular model of the decision situation. Indeed, it is hard to avoid
this logical construction of the decision model once we address ourselves
to the description of a generalized decision situation.

To begin with, we want to know why decisions must be made. The
answer is fairly obvious. The decision-maker wants to achieve something—call it his goal, purpose, objective, or any other synonymous
word. There is, in short, some state of affairs that he wishes to achieve.
Of course, this state of affairs may be the same one that exists for him
at the time of his decision. He may simply be striving for maintenance
of the *status quo*. But, in either case, the decision is made to achieve
some state of affairs.

What does such a decision involve? The decision-maker will choose
an action which he believes will help him most to obtain his objective.
This action will take the form of some kind of utilization of his own
efforts and any resources that he controls. If there is only one course
of action available to him we do not usually speak of a decision problem because the word "decision" implies choice. Therefore, his decision
will consist of the specific utilization of particular resources that he
controls, selected from among all resources that are available to him.
For convenience we will call any such specific utilization of resources
under the decision-maker's control a *strategy*. His decision will consist
of the selection of one of his available strategies.

Recognition of the notorious fact that we do not always achieve our
objectives, despite our best efforts in that direction, leads to another
question: Why may the decision-maker not achieve his objective? The
answer is evident. Certain factors that affect the achievement of objectives are outside the control of the decision-maker.

There are two main classes of such factors. The first is the frequent
intransigence of society and nature. For example, an umbrella manufacturer, faced with the decision problem of how many umbrellas to
make for the coming season, knows that the final outcome of his decision will depend in large measure on the weather conditions that
occur—a factor outside his control. Similarly, the executive of a small
company that uses a basic raw material can scarcely influence the
eventuality of a strike in the suppliers' industry which might close

down the company. Generally, there are a great number of possible combinations of natural, uncontrollable factors that can occur. For simplicity, we will refer to any specific one of these combinations as a *state of nature*.

The second class of uncontrollable factors is the competition of rational opponents. For example, the final outcome of an executive's decision to capture a larger share of the market will usually be affected by actions his competitors take to frustrate his hopes. The same effects are completely apparent in military problems. Generally, there are a great number of different possible competitive actions. Since the specific one that does occur is usually the result of a rational decision process on the part of the competition, it will be convenient to treat these uncontrollable factors as *competitive strategies*, rather than as states of nature. Most managerial decision problems involve both kinds of factors simultaneously.

Our logical analysis of the decision problem has suggested that there are at least three aspects to consider. Let us formulate the decision problem in these terms: The decision-maker wishing to achieve some objective selects a *strategy* from among those available to him. This strategy, together with the *state of nature* that exists, and the *competitive strategy* that occurs, will determine the degree to which his objective is obtained.

THE DECISION PROBLEM

If this theoretical skeleton of the decision situation is at all reasonable, then it should fit the flesh of actual decision problems. Does it? Let us consider some simple (but realistic) decision problems in terms of our logical analysis.

A farmer has a plot of land and he has the objective of achieving the largest profit from it. His available strategies might consist of a variety of crops, any of which he can plant—wheat, corn, soybeans, oats, sugar beets, no crop. His selection from among these strategies is wholly within his control and will constitute his decision. Further, the profit actually obtained will depend not only on the crop he plants but also on a number of factors that are outside his control. Weather is one extremely important example and market price is another, although governmental supports may diminish the importance of this factor to a considerable degree. It seems that the farmer's decision problem fits our model without too much forcing.

The decision problem of an executive responsible for raw-materials inventory is similar. He might have the same objective as the farmer, which is to attain the largest possible amount of profit. His strategies would include various amounts of inventory that he could maintain. Numerous important factors that will determine the amount of profit he actually achieves are outside his control: future availability and price of the raw materials, demand for the finished products, competitive actions, general state of the economy, and so on. His success will depend on the strategy he selects and the state of nature and competitive strategies that actually occur. It appears, again, that the simple framework we have developed fits some actual decision problems.

Up to this point we have tried to discover a suitable framework to describe the general decision problem. In quest of this framework we have examined the input-output model and we have briefly reviewed a number of approaches to the decision problem that have been used by different fields of study. We have not yet considered the basic question: How should the manager select the one strategy he will use from among all the strategies that he is considering? In other words, how does he make his decision?

OBJECTIVES AND UTILITY

The idea of utility introduced by the economists proved to have general appeal to decision theorists. When utility is used as a measurement of the degree to which satisfaction is obtained, then, at least in theory, a number of alternatives can be compared to determine which choice yields the greatest amount of utility. Since satisfaction is not easily measured, a convenient transformation of terms changes the word "satisfaction" into the word "objective." This results in the statement that utility is a measurement of the degree to which an objective is obtained. If the degree of achievement of the objective can be stated in quantitative terms, then alternative choices can be compared with each other. Of course, the supposition made is that satisfaction is directly proportional to the level of attainment of the objective.

Some objectives are either attained or they aren't—with no intermediate possibilities. Good examples can be found in many games. The objective in the game of chess, for example, is to win, and, as the saying goes, "Close only counts in horseshoes." But the more general—and less frivolous—decision problems usually have objectives of such nature that there are vast numbers of degrees of achieving them. This is certainly true of such business objectives as profit or share of market. An executive may have the objective of attaining $1 million gross profit. Naturally, he will be delighted to actually achieve $1.2 million and he may not be too disappointed if he only gets $950,000. Clearly, in this case, there are an enormous number of possible amounts of profit which he might obtain. The fact that his objective is expressed in dollars makes it simple to measure the degree to which the objective is achieved. Frequently the actual dollar profit obtained will be a good measure of degree. Similar remarks can be made about the objective of achieving some specific share of the market.

Not all organizational objectives are of this nature—some are like the game of chess. For example, management involved in a proxy fight for control can have numerous available strategies and there may be many possible states of nature and competitive strategies that affect the final outcome—in short, it is a genuine decision problem that fits our framework. Yet there is only a "yes" or a "no" in terms of achievement of objective. Either management succeeds in retaining control or it fails.

Many organizational objectives have a broad spectrum of possible degrees of achievement but lack a means for measuring them. For example, an important objective in some decision problems may be to achieve and maintain good labor relations. Obviously there are degrees of goodness in labor relations, but how can they be measured? An administrator may have the personal objective of maximum job security. This clearly has degrees also. But how can they be measured?

We have described a range of possibilities. At one extreme, the objective may be achieved or not, with no intermediate possibilities (like a baseball team trying to win the pennant). At the other extreme are objectives that permit a whole range of possible degrees of achievement (like the attendance at a museum). For some objectives there are natural ways of measuring the degree of achievement (counting, weighing, etc.); for others there does not seem to be any obvious way to measure this degree.

FORECASTS AND CONTROL

Certain elements (or variables) or any input-output system can be controlled by the decision-maker. The decision-maker's strategy is a plan of control for these variables. The reason for controlling variables is to attempt to achieve objectives. Good strategies must include the right variables, which means those variables that determine the degree of attainment of the objective. There are many examples of situations in which either the wrong variables are controlled, or not enough of the right ones are considered.

The fact that a number of variables do not lend themselves to managerial control does not mean that they should be ignored. On the contrary, it is a management responsibility to examine all noncontrollable variables that affect the attainment of the objectives. Although the manager cannot exercise control over these variables, he can make *forecasts* about them. The farmer can analyze records of temperature and rainfall to estimate the kind of weather he is likely to experience. The executive in charge of the raw-material inventory can read reports, talk to informed people, observe the actions of other companies that stock the same raw material, and study the history of strikes in the industry that concerns him. Usually both states of nature and competitive strategies can be studied and estimates made to indicate that certain occurrences are more likely than others. Therefore, a good strategy must provide control of the right set of controllable variables, which (based on reasonable forecasts) promises to cope with the right set of uncontrollable variables. Good forecasts are seldom easy to make, nor can the methods for obtaining forecasts be quickly explained. Nevertheless, since forecast and prediction is such a basic requirement of decision-making, and such a fundamental procedure of operations research, we must be prepared to delve deeper into this subject.

Forecasts based on the traditional behavior of a system are only useful if the underlying causes of the system's history are unchanged. We call this a stable system, recognizing that the pattern of stability may be far from simple. In some cases it might exist, but in such complex form that it hasn't been discovered. The pattern must be known (e.g., seasonal fluctuation, growth at a fixed rate of increase, an operating level that is unchanging over time, etc.) if a forecast is to have meaning.

Since forecasting involves procedures that cost money, it must be assumed that a rational manager would expect to get a return that more than compensates him (in some sense) for this expense. One great strength of decision theory is that the *value* of information generated to provide forecasts and support predictions can be compared with the cost of obtaining it. The decision of how much to spend in this way is a decision problem in its own right and is amenable to analysis.

FUNCTIONS AND DISTRIBUTIONS

The managerial objective is a particular kind of a variable. It must be a variable, since if it were a constant, with only one possible value, the decision-maker would have no choice of a value for the objective and no problem to solve. The objective is called a *dependent* variable because the value that it takes depends on the values of the other variables in the system. These other variables, which are called *independent* variables, are the many controllable and noncontrollable factors which we have previously discussed.

A mathematical description of these variables and their relations can be written. At once, it shows both the economy of the compact mathematical form and the advantage of such representation for generalizing any situation. The equation which models this situation is $y = f(x, z)$. The letter x is an abstraction that stands for all independent, controllable variables. (It could be order quantities in an inventory study or an amount of fertilizer to be used by the farmer.) Our symbol z represents all independent, noncontrollable variables. We associate a forecast with the range of z's that can occur. (For the inventory example this would be forecasts of demand; the farmer might choose to vary his fertilizer according to the forecasts of precipitation.) The dependent variable is y. It is our objective (perhaps cost to be minimized in the inventory problem or yield to be maximized by the farmer). The equation can be written out in words, *viz.*, the dependent variable y is (=) a function of (f) the independent variables x and z.

The fact that we write a mathematical equation does not mean that the variables must be quantifiable, for useful information is conveyed by the equation itself. For example, consider the following statement. Customer goodwill is a function of speed of delivery, quality and price of merchandise, and his relations with our salesmen as compared with those of our competitors. Although this model *lacks quantification* of terms it *provides a systematic view of relations*.

Now let us look at a function which does lend itself to quantitative representation. We can, for example, choose profit as our objective. The generalized function would be: Total profit $(p) = f[\text{unit sales price}$ (s); unit cost (c); number of items sold $(n)]$, i.e., $p = f(s, c, n)$. In this case, we know the exact function: $p = n(s - c)$.

On the face of it, unit sales price and unit cost are controllable, while the number of items sold (n) is noncontrollable. Actually, we can exercise some control over the sales volume (n), since the number of items sold $= f(\text{unit sales price})$. Unit sales price is under our control—so to some extent we can regulate the number of items sold. Looking at unit cost, there is a threshold below which we cannot even manufacture an item. Above the threshold, cost and quality are tightly related. As we cut cost we impair quality. Also, lower quality may result in a smaller number of items sold, i.e., quality $= f(\text{unit cost})$. This means that the number of items sold $= f(\text{unit cost})$. Further, unit cost includes advertising and promotion, which means that in yet another way $n = f(c)$.

Most functions are complex in the fashion that we have illustrated above, but that is not all. Some severe accounting problems occur. Unit cost is not obvious; the appropriate measure is difficult to obtain. Fixed costs (such as advertising and administrative overhead) are not easily allocated on a per unit cost basis. You should be able to explain why this is so.

It is apparent from our example of the simple profit function $p = n(s - c)$ that dependencies exist among the independent variables. The achievement of an objective requires the full consideration of the inter-relationships among independent variables as well as direct relationships that affect the dependent variable. Also, a penetrating understanding of the measurement (e.g., accounting) problems is required before any solution can be obtained.

Degree of control is strongly affected by degree of predictability. We may, at best, have the notion that as price goes up the number of items sold goes down. (Of course this is not an inflexible rule since there are cases of items that may increase in sales volume with increasing price. Can you think of one?) Over a period of time, the manager will probably have accumulated enough data to plot the relationship between sales price and sales volume. Figure 2.4 depicts a strong relationship with sales volume decreasing as price goes up.

The problem here is that each point represents a different month so that some points occur in the spring, which may be the best selling time. Every point has a seasonal component, and if seasonal variation is important, that would obscure the relationship between sales price and sales volume. Similarly, competitors' prices in each month may have affected the number of items sold. Many other factors also could influence the relationship under study. The ability to predict sales volume as a function of sales price is determined by the extent to which

FIGURE 2.4 Data from past observations indicate that sales volume tends to decrease as price increase.

all the pertinent factors can be taken into account. Seldom can we expect to obtain an exact relationship.

Variables that are essentially noncontrollable can be studied initially by means of simple frequency distributions. The use of such distributions can result in surprisingly good forecasts. For example, an executive has collected the (hypothetical) data in Table 2.1 concerning absenteeism. It has been tabulated as a frequency distribution in Table 2.1 and plotted in Figure 2.5.

TABLE 2.1

Number of times a worker is absent for a single day in a summer month or winter month	*Number of workers with the given number of absences*	
	SUMMER MONTH	WINTER MONTH
0	2	368
1	21	368
2	136	184
3	341	61
4	362	15
5	120	3
6	17	1
7	1	0

The shapes of these curves are well known, the summer chart illustrating a normal distribution and the winter chart showing a Poisson distribution. Many characteristics of these distributions have been carefully studied by the methods of mathematical statistics, and this large body of knowledge can be put to work to achieve useful predictions of future expectations.

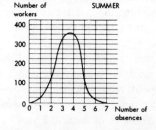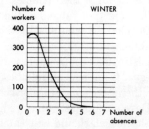

FIGURE 2.5 A comparison of the number of times a worker is absent for a single day in a summer month and a winter month.

The stability characteristics of noncontrollable variables must be examined before we can put together measures of utility, objectives, variables, functions, and distributions in an integrated decision-theory framework. As was previously mentioned, data that are used to make forecasts and predictions are always assumed to be derived from a stable process. The distribution is said to describe a particular situation that holds constant throughout the period in which the data are collected and, of course, into the period of the forecast. Sometimes a frequency distribution gives evidence that a change took place during the period of observation. For example, the bimodal distribution shown in Figure 2.6 could have come from a process that produces a bimodal

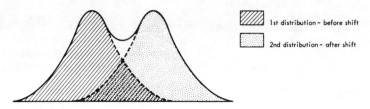

FIGURE 2.6 The bimodal distribution can arise from an unstable process.

distribution. On the other hand, it might represent two aspects of an unstable normal distribution where a shift took place during the period of observation. Predictions and forecasts based on unstable processes (where this fact is not known) can lead to serious mistakes.

MAXIMIZATION PRINCIPLES

We are now prepared to examine the decision-maker's sequence of operations up to this point.

1. Choose the objective; specify its dimension and value.
2. Isolate all of the variables that are pertinent to the attainment of the objective value, i.e., the relevant independent variables.
3. Develop the relationships that exist between the independent variables.
4. Distinguish controllable variables (which can be part of the strategy) from noncontrollable variables (classifying the latter as either states of nature or competitive strategies).
5. Develop forecasts and predictions for the noncontrollable variables, which should be treated as states of nature. Those variables which have (rational) intelligence behind them must be treated separately by game theoretic methods.

6. Determine whether or not the forecasts and predictions are based on stable processes. This determination can be intuitive but powerful methods of statistical quality control are available to assist.
7. Develop the function that relates the independent variables to the dependent objective variable.
8. State the restrictions that limit the possible values of controllable variables.
9. Choose those values of the controllable variables (i.e., that strategy) which promise to maximize the degree of attainment of the objective, within the limits set by the restrictions.

In point 1 above, we stated that a specific dimension and value should be chosen for the objective. For example, our objective may have the dimension of profit, and the chosen value of profit might be $500,000. Frequently it is not feasible to select a specific numerical value for the objective. Sometimes it is not even desirable. An alternative formulation is to substitute for the numerical value the requirement of a "best possible," or *optimal* value. Where the objective is a variable measured along a continuous scale, the distinguishing property of an optimal value will be direction. In other words, optimal will sometimes be the greatest possible or *maximal* value while at other times it will be the least possible or *minimal* value.

Although it may be reasonable to select $500,000 as our profit objective, the manager would be overlooking the possibility that his company's profits might be greater. The difference between $500,000 and some larger attainable value would be an *opportunity cost*. This cost of foregone opportunity should be minimized for an optimal solution. Opportunity costs, which we shall discuss again, are penalties suffered for not having done the best possible thing. So, although it is perfectly reasonable to choose that strategy which will result in $500,000 profit, this type of approach is seldom likely to produce an optimal decision.

Optimal decision procedures can always be stated as a maximization problem. The quantity that is always being maximized is the degree of attainment of the objective. Let us consider three cases. The first requires no translation: Our objective is profit and we wish to maximize it. The second is more complex: Our objective is to achieve some in-between scale value which is associated with a zero opportunity cost. Here are a few examples of situations where neither of the extremal points of a scale are desirable. (a) The most comfortable height for a car seat is (say) 14″. (b) 98.6 degrees is the optimal body temperature. As temperature increases or decreases from that standard, there are increasingly severe opportunity costs. (c) The optimal balance between acid and base in a carbonated soft drink is a neutral solution (i.e., $pH = 7$). (d) A want ad reads: Applicants for the police force should be between the following ages —— and heights ——.

In all of these cases, *deviations* from the ideal must be measured and should be minimized—which leads us to the third case. The dimension is cost (either type—real or opportunity) and we want to minimize it. This problem is equivalent to maximizing $(K -$ cost) where K is any constant including zero. For example, assume that we wish to minimize the (real) cost of selling a certain product. As we find ways to lower the cost we increase the degree of attainment. The minimum cost for selling the product represents the maximum attainment of the objective. It is also the point at which zero opportunity cost occurs. We note, however, that it is not the point of zero real cost. The nonoptimal, minimum real cost is zero. But under normal circumstances zero real cost means that no product can be made at all. This is certainly not a reasonable objective, whereas zero opportunity cost is. Therefore, the minimization of real cost is not a sensible objective until *restrictions* are placed on the means for obtaining it. In the same way, maximum dollar profit is seldom desired at the expense of goodwill, future profits, or a jail sentence.

Restrictions are a natural part of a complex objective. All real objectives are complex, because they never involve just one variable. Whenever we say that we wish to attain some end, we do so with all kinds of if's, and's, and but's. However, it isn't an easy matter to visualize and enumerate the total set of objectives at the very beginning of a problem. As much as possible, point 1 should specify multiple objectives, but point 8 takes into consideration the fact that certain restrictions become apparent only after the full set of relationships among variables has been investigated.

Generally speaking, degree of attainment can be maximized for only one objective at a time. In other words, if we wish to maximize sales volume we can seldom expect to maximize profit at the same time. That is why we speak of an *objective* and *restrictions*. For example, maximization of sales volume is subject to the restriction that profit does not fall below P_1, or that profit falls between P_1 and P_2.[1]

---

[1] In linear programming problems, the objective variable has a symmetric relationship with another, different variable, which is automatically minimized when the objective is maximized, and vice versa. This characteristic is known as *duality*. In general, the dual variable provides information about an economic aspect of the problem that might not ordinarily be considered, but which is exceedingly useful.

Point 5 requires that variables belonging to states of nature should be separated from variables belonging to intelligent competitors. The reason for this is that all decision-makers are trying to maximize their respective degrees of attainment. Such problems of conflict between rational opponents require special methods which are treated by the theory of games. If it is possible for a company to determine that its competitors will not behave in a rational manner, then competitive strategies should be treated as states of nature, where forecasts and predictions will be most valuable. The value of information for forecasting and predicting (obtained, for example, through espionage) becomes of paramount importance. Under many circumstances, if the competitor is rational no forecast is required. An analysis in game theory terms is essential. This approach is particularly important when competitors are striving for identical objectives, e.g., brand share. In any case, it is always important to remember that others may be trying to achieve maximization at our expense. We are seldom alone in choosing strategies and the decisions of others can seriously affect our own attainments.

PROBLEMS

1. Develop the input-output model for an electric typewriter. How does this differ from a mechanical typewriter? What control is exercised over the inputs? What feedback exists? Transform the output into the input of a corresponding system.

2. Develop the input-output model for a warehouse. Assume that the decision to reorder is made by an executive in the company's main office, which is 300 miles away from the warehouse. Design an automatic regulator to relieve management of this reorder function. How will exceptions to the procedure be handled?

3. Management has three brand names picked out for a new product, four different package designs, and four different advertising campaigns. How many different strategies are being considered? What possible states of nature could affect the choice? To what extent can competitive strategies be taken into account?

4. Using the data of Table 2.1 and Figure 2.5, draw the distribution that would apply to the fall season if the change between seasons were regular and continuous. Under these assumptions would spring and fall be the same? How many extra workers would you hire in the summer if demand for the product were constant throughout the year? How do these considerations relate to the decision framework?

5. As far as possible, apply the nine steps of the decision-maker's sequence to the following situations: management must either build a new plant or expand their present facilities; a company must replace a sales manager who is retiring; repeated complaints of bad service are received by a department store; top management requests a full report on the possibilities of bidding for government contracts; the governors of three states must agree on a site for a new airport.

6. A company that has one plant produces a variety of items for sale to the public. Their situation is conceptualized in the diagram below:

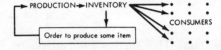

The responsible manager establishes policies which determine when an order shall be transmitted to the production department, which will require the fabrication of a specific item in a given quantity. The procedure is very much like the furnace-thermostat feedback system discussed in the text. The established policies usually require that an order be made when the inventory of an item falls to a certain level. The policy also establishes how much shall be produced. In analogy to the furnace-thermostat example, these two levels are equivalent to the temperatures at which the furnace will turn on and off.

 a. What objectives are involved in the decisions setting these two levels?
 b. Suppose demand for some item has large fluctuations around an average which is constant for a long period of time. How does this affect the ·levels?
 c. Suppose demand has very small fluctuations around its average but that the average is increasing steadily. How does this affect the levels?
 d. What if one item has extremely high labor costs. How does this affect the levels?
 e. Under what conditions will the inventory carried be eliminated?

7. Classify the following objectives according to whether there are degrees of attainment and whether the degree of attainment is measurable:

 a. A salesman's objective of increasing his sales enough to win a company prize.
 b. A financial executive's objective of obtaining a $1,000,000 bank loan.
 c. A salesman's objective of obtaining a large account.
 d. A salesman's objective of making a large nonrepeat sale to a customer.
 e. An organization's objective of achieving a required minimum percentage of employee participation in a health insurance program.
 f. A hospital administrator's objective of achieving the lowest possible labor turnover.

   g. An advertising agency's objective not to lose clients.

   h. The same agency's objective to gain new clients.

   i. The research department manager's belief that pure research should constitute at least 10 per cent of the R & D budget.

   j. The president's announced intention to reduce government work from its present level of 80 per cent of the company's annual revenue.

8. Are there many organizational situations that you can think of which involve feedback? Name some and describe these operations.

9. How many different objectives can you think of which a sales manager might have? How many are quantifiable with regard to degree of attainment?

10. From the standpoint of advertising policies the totality of potential customers constitutes a black box. We have advertising as input and demand as output. Thus:

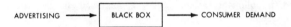

ADVERTISING ⟶ BLACK BOX ⟶ CONSUMER DEMAND

The effect of advertising depends on the unknown circuitry of the black box. In order to determine advertising policies we would like to know something about the effect of the input-advertising, on the output-demand. If we really know nothing about the black box circuitry we can only get information by varying the input and then observing the output.

   a. We can change the input or not change it, and the output can either change or not change. Thus, there are four possible combinations. Without saying anything about the size or the direction of the changes involved, what can you conclude (if anything) from each of the four possible cases?

   b. Suppose the output changes in the same direction as the input but that very large input changes produce only small output changes. What does this imply?

   c. Suppose the circuitry is very complicated and there is a considerable time delay before changes in input show up in the form of output changes. Suppose, further, that this time delay is unknown. What effect does this have on our reasoning? What mistakes might it produce?

      Consider the analogy of controlling water temperature when taking a shower. Suppose the pipes leading to the shower are so long that ten seconds are required before a change in the amount of hot water reaches the shower. Now suppose you are impatient and only wait five seconds. What will happen?

   d. In terms of this model, what is wrong with the policy of setting a regional monthly advertising budget as a percentage of the preceding month's sales for the region?

11. Clonus is defined as "a forced series of alternating contractions and partial relaxations of the same muscle." An eye twitch, for example, is not under the command of the brain and might be described as a runaway feedback situation. Does this model have any applicability to a business situation? What might it have to do with cybernetics?

12. Construct an input-output feedback model for an airplane under automatic control. Relate this analogy—emphasizing differences as well as similarities—to the activities of:

   a. A medical research department.
   b. A library information recovery system.
   c. A geological team searching for petroleum.
   d. The group in charge of blending paints to obtain "exact" color matching.

13. The new product manager of your company has presented an idea for a chocolate flavored toothpaste. At the product presentation meeting he offered the following rationale, "It just might go and the cost to the company of trying it is very low."

   "Not so," you said. "You are only talking about the real costs of this attempt versus a failure. What about the opportunity costs?" Would you please explain in more detail what you mean—to the president.

14. My car can go as fast as 120 mph. The speed limit on the highway is 65. What is my opportunity cost if I'm going 50?

15. What function should be maximized if the objective is

   a. To win at bingo.
   b. To keep the house at 68 degrees.
   c. To never carry more than 2 ounces of change in one's coat pocket?

   What potential strategies might be available in each case?

3 | The Objectives of Decisions

As we have seen in the preceding chapter, a rational approach to the decision problem must reflect the manager's objectives. The problem formulation stems from the question: Why make a decision at all? And the answer embodies the desire of the decision-maker to achieve some future state of affairs—his objective. He must choose one strategy in preference to all other alternatives and this choice can only be made rationally in terms of the objective. Thus, the precise formulation of the objective is the first, major problem facing the manager. Consequently, our first concern will be with the difficulties and problems involved in formulating objectives.

We have already suggested that some objectives seem easy to quantify, others are not quantifiable, and a great number fall in the middle ground between these two types. These differences are important because the quantitative analysis of a decision problem requires measurement—a numerical description of each alternative strategy.[1] Only in this way can several strategies be compared. Apart from this consideration there are other paramount issues concerning objectives that require careful analysis. The various ambiguities and difficulties that characterize objectives must be explored to delineate the possibilities of using a rational approach to the decision problem.

---

[1] This does *not* mean that costs and/or benefits must always be measured. See, e.g., Miller and Starr, "Inventory Problems with Unknown Costs," *Executive Decisions and Operations Research* (Englewood Cliffs, N.J.: Prentice-Hall, Inc., 1960), Sec. 87.

GOALS, PURPOSES, AND RATIONAL BEHAVIOR

The formulation of objectives cannot be viewed as independent of some major ethical questions, which might be expected inasmuch as classical philosophy sought to discover the steps to be taken for a *good* life. And what is this idea of the good life if not an objective to be achieved? In fact, the classical conception of rationality was defined as the ability to select means to achieve goals or objectives. This line of reasoning was subsequently subjected to serious questioning.

First, extending the definition of rationality led to the interpretation of everything in terms of the purpose it fulfilled. Thus, the argument ran, if one saw a watch, one could infer the existence of a watchmaker. Similarly, if one sees an ear one must infer the existence of an ear-maker (who designed that ear to achieve its purpose of hearing). This is called *teleological* reasoning. Interpretations of this sort were what Aristotle called the "final causes" of the events. Such arguments may have had their place in religion and philosophy but they tend to impede scientific analysis. One of Darwin's major contributions was the demonstration that remarkable adaptation to environment could result from the interplay of a great number of essentially random factors. In short, he showed that it was unnecessary to assume *final* causes to understand the adaptation of organisms to their environments.

Another argument against this approach arose from the *positivistic* movement in science. A human being "introspects" and believes that he has purposefully selected means to achieve his objectives. But it is also easy to assume purposefulness in the behavior of a hungry white rat. Psychological studies have thrown doubt on human purposefulness in at least some situations where humans think they are being purposeful. In any event, positivism in science required that conclusions be based only on observable evidence. In psychology this took the form of the ruthless elimination of introspection as a source of valid scientific information. The school of psychology that represented this position to the fullest extreme is known as *behaviorism*, from the fact that only the observable behavior of the subject is studied. (It seems apt to note that someone once said, "behaviorism is being willing to discuss the scratch—but not the itch.") The net effect of the positivistic movement was to strongly prejudice scientists against ascribing rationality to goal-seeking behavior.

OPEN SYSTEMS

Recent developments in science serve to confirm the fact that rationality cannot be identified with purposeful selection of means to achieve desired ends. The biologist Ludwig von Bertalanffy has introduced and extensively analyzed a new class of systems, which he calls "open systems." There are many interesting characteristics of such systems. For our purposes the most important of these is the fact that such a system will appear to be goal-seeking, although it is not, in any sense of the word, "rational." Certain chemical solutions provide good examples of open systems. But von Bertalanffy has found even more interesting examples in organisms and higher order organizational systems which are formed of living creatures—for example, human society.

The reason that the system appears to be goal-seeking, despite the lack of any cerebral rationality behind it, is that an equilibrium exists among its component parts. Any disturbance of this equilibrium initiates compensating reactions which immediately lead to the establishment of a new equilibrium. In other words, the system will search[2] for equilibrium every time its balance is disturbed.

A great many human objectives can be defined in terms of such equilibrium. To what extent can the search by humans for objectives be understood in terms of the dynamic equilibrium-seeking process of open systems? This kind of questioning about open systems is not purely theoretical. It has been convincingly demonstrated by W. Ross Ashby, who designed and built a device which he named the Homeostat. Ashby's machine is a complicated piece of electrical circuitry which will hunt for equilibrium whenever it is disturbed. Significantly, it will find equilibrium conditions which were not intentionally built into the device by its maker. Therefore, when the device has achieved a new equilibrium, no one, including the designer, will know what circuits it has completed in order to achieve the equilibrium. Similar devices have now been constructed by others. Some of them exhibit the most disconcertingly "lifelike" behavior while in pursuit of their objectives. And yet there is no rationality in any of them. It has become clear, then, that the appearance of rationality does not guarantee the actual existence of an underlying rational choice system.

These remarks may not seem relevant to any study of organizational

---

[2] Words like search, hunt, remember and goal-seek can be attributed to purely mechanistic systems in an anthropomorphic fashion because of the apparent correspondence between the observable systems actions and those of human beings.

objectives. However, upon inspection they are not at all far-fetched. The conclusion that one reaches is that an open system will find equilibrium if left by itself. However, if the process by which the system achieves equilibrium is continually disturbed by "rational" efforts, it may well produce an inherent instability and the equilibrium may never be achieved. The national economy, for example, is an enormously complex organization which may well have many characteristics of open systems. A frequently stated national economic objective is the achievement of prosperity without inflation. Since the quantity of money in circulation plays a fundamental role in the state of the national economy, the Federal Reserve System uses its control over the money supply to attempt to achieve the national objective. The means it uses, such as changes in the discount rate, are well known.

A number of economists maintain that the rational efforts of the Federal Reserve System are of no avail and perhaps worse than useless. Some hold that an appropriate policy should be fixed in advance and then adhered to by the Federal Reserve System. In other words, no policy changes should be made because of changing economic conditions. If, indeed, the national economy is an open system, then it would adapt to change while maintaining the national objectives as part of its own search for equilibrium. Consequently, our national objectives would have a better chance of being achieved. Similar notions can be applied to many types of organizations.

We shall present a brief illustration of a business system that regains equilibrium after it has been disturbed. Consider the case of a mail-order company which solicits new customers by means of direct mail. (To avoid obscuring the main point we have not introduced random variation in the hypothetical data.) The company mails 800 letters each week and obtains orders from 1 per cent of the mailing. The repeat-order rate is constant. One-half of each week's new customers reorder in the second week, one-fourth reorder in the third week, one-eighth reorder in the fourth week, and so on. Table 3.1 shows how the generation of orders, composed of new-customer orders and repeat orders, reaches an equilibrium value of 15 orders per day. Now, let us suppose that in weeks 8 and 9 the company experiences an unusually heavy response. This raises the total orders handled for a period of six weeks. At the end of that time, by the fourteenth week, total orders have returned to equilibrium. Figure 3.1 shows how the system gradually returns to equilibrium.

Actually, a system of this type is always being disturbed by random variation in both the number of new customers and the reorder rates.

However, if the random variation comes from a stable process, then the system is continually hunting for its equilibrium value. If a basic change takes place, then the system adopts a new equilibrium value as its focus, while responding to all random disturbances. An attempt by management to maintain total orders at 15 per week by controlling the number of letters mailed or by providing incentives to increase the repeat order rate can result in far greater fluctuation than would occur if the system were left alone. Only when management fully understands the nature of the system with which it is dealing can it provide rational policy decisions that might improve the performance of the system.

TABLE 3.1 Generation of orders of a mail-order house.

Week Number	1	2	3	4	5	6	7	8	9	10	11	12	13	14	15	16
Number of new customers	8	8	8	8	8	8	8	20	20	8	8	8	8	8	8	8
First repeat order		4	4	4	4	4	4	4	10	10	4	4	4	4	4	4
Second repeat order			2	2	2	2	2	2	2	5	5	2	2	2	2	2
Third repeat order				1	1	1	1	1	1	1	2	2	1	1	1	1
Fourth repeat order				—	—	—	—	—	—	—	—	1	1	—	—	—
Total orders	8	12	14	15	15	15	15	27	33	24	19	17	16	15	15	15

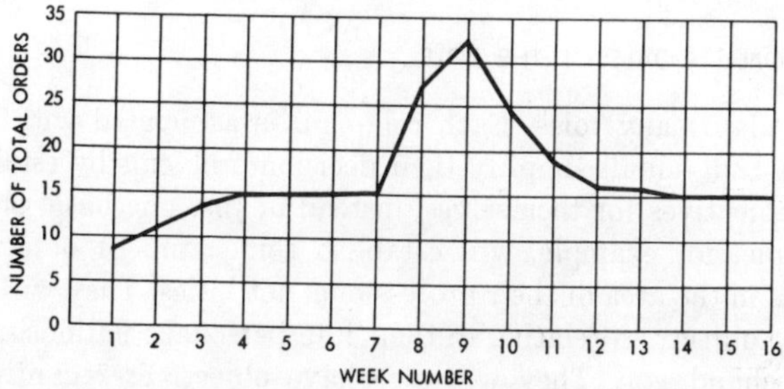

FIGURE 3.1 The system returns to equilibrium after disturbance.

From examples such as this, we learn that it is not necessarily the case that all objectives can be, or should be, achieved by rational selection of specific means to a given end. If we cannot identify rational behavior by observing the means that are chosen to achieve a particular goal, can we recognize rationality by examining the objectives themselves?

GOALS OF THE INDIVIDUAL

Organizational objectives coexist with the objectives of individuals who compose the organization. They are not the same. Our intention is to analyze the way in which objectives at different levels in the organization interact with each other. It seems reasonable to begin with the individual—the smallest entity in the organization.

The goals of individuals have been the subject of discussion and debate for many centuries. To say that happiness is the goal of the individual (a frequent suggestion) does not solve any problem. We cannot define happiness in operational terms. Operationalism is an important, underlying concept of operations research. It implies concreteness, the ability to observe, measure, and analyze. Since an analysis of the operations that must take place or be performed in order to be happy cannot be accomplished, we cannot treat happiness as an operational term. Satisfactory measurements cannot even be made to distinguish between degrees of happiness. Although each of us can testify to the fact that happiness exists, we cannot transform our awareness to concrete terms. Similar problems result from other suggested choices such as satisfaction, contentment, and comfort as fundamental objectives of individuals. Since life is too short to follow the arguments of philosophers in a book that is intended to be operationally useful, we must consider other ways of examining the goals of individuals.

OPERATIONAL GOALS OF THE ROLE

People play many roles. Each role can be associated with its own objectives. Individuals simplify their decision problems by establishing multiple objectives for themselves, instead of just one basic objective. Most people, for example, will establish some kind of objective for themselves in the area of their professional activities. They will usually have other objectives relating to their interpersonal relationships; e.g., father, husband, son. They will also have objectives regarding their relationship to society as a whole, e.g., political activity or public-spirited work. They will often have some objectives regarding their leisure activities. And, of course, we can continue and obtain quite a catalogue of the areas in which people are likely to set themselves different kinds of goals. It appears that most people handle their decision problems in a particular field of activity by ignoring the objectives of other fields of activity. Thus, a manager will solve his professional decision problems—for example, what position he will accept—in terms of his career objectives. This does not preclude other influences, but suggests that they frequently act more like constraints than fundamental objectives.

Within any single field of activity an individual has many different roles. An administrator reports to his boss and in turn has people reporting to him. His position in the organization determines the extent of his responsibility and the range and importance of the decisions he must make. The goal of the administrator is strongly tied to the complex image he has of his role within the organization. Although no two managers have identical situations, the similarity of goals which they share as a group allows us to generalize about managerial goals. At the same time, we cannot be blind to the differences. Similarly, we can group employee goals, stockholder's goals, salesmen's goals, and so on. There are certain relevant patterns of goal-seeking within each of these groups which hardly require expansion here. Of great interest are those cases where a significant conflict exists between the objectives of at least two groups to which the individual belongs.

CONFLICT BETWEEN GOALS

The manager has various roles and each role has its objectives. The groups and subgroups to which he belongs have organizational objectives. Conflicts between goals can occur in a number of ways: (1) conflicts between the individual's roles, (2) conflicts between group objectives, and (3) conflicts between the individual's role and the group objectives.

Looking at conflicts of the first type, an individual cannot confine his attention to the objectives of one field of activities and ignore the other parts of his life. A new position that satisfies a professional objective may entail relocation, which puts stresses and strains on family relationships. In this event, the individual must attempt to weigh his different objectives, one against the other. It is difficult to do this because there is no single, underlying objective that suffices as a means of measuring the unified importance of the different objectives. Nevertheless, people have to resolve such problems many times in their lives.

In some conceptual way they manage to evaluate their alternatives across a range of objectives. Perhaps this is done in some unified terms of potential for happiness. But if so, there are serious difficulties and possible contradictions involved in this notion of happiness.

Considering the second kind of conflict, an individual can participate in two groups that have conflicting objectives. He may not even be aware of the fact because his roles in each group are not in conflict. This point demonstrates that an individual is not compelled to identify entirely with and share completely the objectives of an organization. Furthermore, he would seldom weight the groups of which he is a member as being of equal importance. For example, an employee who participates in a stock-purchasing plan is part owner of the company in which he works. When this employee demands higher wages, he is, in effect, reducing the dividend which he can receive as a stockholder. Usually, the employee does not consider his role in the ownership group to be as important as his role as an employee. Whenever the individual's role objectives strongly coincide with conflicting objectives of groups to which he belongs, the result is either conflict between roles (within the individual) or between the individual and (at least) one of the groups. In the latter case, which is the third type of conflict, the individual withdraws from the organization that he feels he is in conflict with. He may also try to change the conflicting group's objectives.

SUBOPTIMIZATION

If there is no conflict between objectives, the manager can proceed to solve each decision problem separately. As long as the action taken to achieve either objective is independent of the other, he can separate them. However, when objectives are dependent, the optimization of one can result in a lower degree of attainment for at least some of the others. This condition is known as *suboptimization*.

For example, an executive may decide to take a new position on the basis of his professional objectives which entails extremely long hours and much traveling. Although the new job is optimal in terms of the executive's professional objectives, the time he can now spend with his family is sharply reduced. This may have such adverse effects that the executive will find that his optimization in terms of one objective has produced an overall result which is much less than optimal in terms of all his objectives.

The notion of suboptimization is also involved in the effects of time on the decision problem. We lead our lives through time but have only imperfect ability to foretell the future. Each decision problem must be solved for a foreseeable future based on present knowledge and the situation that currently obtains. However, the action chosen is likely to have effects on the decision-maker's situation for a considerable period in the future. An optimal action as of today may, therefore, turn out to produce a serious suboptimization in terms of a longer period of time.

Consider, for example, the decision problem of an engineering student who must select a set of courses for his electives. His professional objective is to become as good an engineer as he possibly can be, so he decides to use all of his electives on additional engineering courses. At the time, this decision appears to be a legitimate optimization of professional objectives. Some years later this engineer may discover that stultification can result from too narrow specialization and that this may have had serious consequences on his lifetime objectives (e.g., his ability to achieve satisfactory interpersonal relationships, his desire to have a well-rounded life, and, surprisingly, even on his career objective of professional advancement). The engineer's decision may have resulted in severely suboptimal conditions upon which to build his future (even in the same field of activity).

Clearly, we can never really achieve optimization. Over time, unexpected events can change what may have appeared to be an optimal decision into an inferior one. There is almost no reversibility in many important decision systems. By the time we learn that a decision was not a good one, we can no longer return to the state which prevailed before the decision was made. Consequently, decisions must be based on the best possible predictions of future expectations. In addition, our decision procedures should not commit us to irrevocable commitments for long periods of time. And so we reach the conclusion that a rational decision process should include the consideration of sequence. Such a *sequential decision process* permits maximum flexibility with respect to an evolution of both objectives and actions in a quasi-predictable world.

BOUNDED RATIONALITY

We have been using the notion of an "optimum," rather loosely. People rarely make a prolonged effort to achieve the optimum action in any realistic decision problem facing them. To paraphrase John Maurice Clark, people simply don't have such an irrational passion for dispassionate rationality. And there are good reasons why they shouldn't. These reflect the exorbitant complexity of many realistic decision problems. Three main aspects of this complexity might be noted.

First, an optimum decision, made at one point in time, is generally suboptimum in terms of subsequent times. Since we are limited in our ability to foresee the future it follows that it is useless to go to extreme lengths to search for the "most optimum" decision. It is complex enough to decide how far to go.

Second, there are frequently an enormous number of possible choices of actions (strategies). Any attempt to obtain information about all of them would be self-defeating. Consider the decision problem of the executive looking for a new job. Should he attempt to catalogue every available position in the world from which to choose the best one? If he tried he would die of old age before he got all of the necessary information. Furthermore, even as he collected the information it would change. While waiting for new opportunities the old ones would disappear. Until when should he defer his decision?

Third, there are virtually innumerable factors outside the control of the decision-maker. These states of nature affect the decision outcome. It would be impossible to list all of them let alone to determine the totality of their effects in order to determine the optimum action. Often the necessary information just isn't available. The umbrella manufacturer (generally) would not attempt to examine the effects of limited war, nuclear holocausts, prolonged depression, or an explosion of the sun on the outcomes of his decision regarding the number of umbrellas to make. He must assume some reasonable kind of natural stability and act accordingly.

The net effect of the limitations on human decision-making procedures has been observed and neatly summarized by Herbert Simon in his "principle of bounded rationality." According to this principle, human beings seldom try to find *the* optimum action in a decision problem. Instead, they define in a limited sense the ranges of outcomes (that probably could be delivered by their available strategies) which would be good enough. Then they select a strategy that is likely to achieve one of the good-enough sets of outcomes. Thus, the executive looking for a new job makes no effort to discover all possible jobs from which to select the optimum one. Instead, he decides in quite broad terms what he wants from a job. His searching will provide him with an adequate range of the things he wants, e.g., sufficient income, satisfactory working conditions, reasonable chance for advancement. He does not try to find the one job that exists somewhere in the world which will give him the *present* optimum. Also, there is always some new opportunity that may become available tomorrow. How long should he wait —for the three-, five-, or twenty-year optimum? The principle of bounded rationality is a straightforward way to describe the *actual* decision procedures of human beings. This principle succinctly reminds us not to assume an irrational extreme of rationality.

It is always questionable whether the optimum procedure is to search for *the* optimum value, and this is a paradox of sorts. Even looking backward, the concept of a personal, lifetime optimum is impossible to measure. Optimums are like Holy Grails; part of their existence is in the seeking. Because of the nature of values, they may disappear as they are found. Apparent optimums are encountered which turn out to be like reflections of bent mirrors or partial truths based on transient identifications and evanescent realities. In this sense, bounded rationality, as an approach, may bring one closer to the *ultimate optimum* than direct searches for *immediate optimums*. This was the essence of the psychotherapeutic position known as Couéism. Emile Coué (born in France in 1857) excited widespread excitement in the 1920's with his notion that "Every day in every way, I am getting better and better." There is evidence that the acceptable increments were too small. Nevertheless, over time, both individuals and groups may be better off to move in incremental steps of reasonable size toward the perceived and bounded optimum than in giant strides based on long-range perceptions of where the ultimate optimal exists. The size of a reasonable step and the amount of bounding that is rational are issues that pertain to all decision systems.

PRINCIPLES AND MAXIMS: A RESERVOIR OF HEURISTICS

The difficulties involved in even simple decision problems can appear to be enormous. Yet both introspection and observation indicate that people will attempt to be rational (in the sense of achieving as much as they can) in their selection of actions, despite all the problems. Fortunately, an important source of assistance is available. Aside from outer space, today no one is the first to have to face any specific type of decision problem (and even there we wonder). Millions of people have known the same types of problems in times past. Society has accumulated an immense store of information concerning the nature of problems, their possible solutions, and approaches to these solutions.

This *wisdom* is stored in many forms, including ethical rules, principles, and maxims which warn us to consider certain factors in certain ways— or to proceed at our own risk.

Maxims are no guarantee of success. Often they are contradictory. "Look before you leap" says one, but "He who hesitates is lost." Both maxims remind us that the speed with which we reach a decision may be an important factor.

Consider Kant's dictum, *viz.*, we should always treat others as ends in themselves rather than as means to our own ends. This suggests that many apparent "optimizing" actions subsequently redound to our disadvantage, i.e., turn out to have been a suboptimization. The Golden Rule is another codification. It specifies how one should govern his choice of actions, lest he end by suboptimizing his (over time) overall objectives. Lacking sufficient information about a situation, the Golden Rule ("do unto others as you would have others do to you," Matt. 7:12; Luke 6:31) is a good heuristic.[3] The word heuristic is derived from the Greek *heuriskin* meaning "serving to discover." The closest definition we can give for it—with respect to current usage—is that a heuristic is an operational maxim. And by this we mean that it promises the *best* potential *sub*optimization for a variety of circumstances too complex and/or too future to permit total rationality.

Ethical maxims provide a necessary and powerful pressure that forces us to consider whether our objectives are reasonable. An eight-year-old boy's major objective may be to eat a maximum number of chocolate candies. If one speaks to him of the pleasures of marriage he may ask if it is like eating chocolates. Fortunately, society offers us a great deal of advice to the effect that we should not commit ourselves wholly to the pleasures of eating chocolates, because we may subsequently find that it was not a satisfactory overall objective.

SUMMARY OF THE INDIVIDUALS GOAL-SEEKING CHARACTERISTICS

Let us examine what we have discovered by considering the decision procedures of individuals involved in the business of living.

1. Being unable to satisfactorily describe goals in terms of *one* ob-

---

[3] Our statement concerning the decision oriented view of the Golden Rule that appeared in D. Miller and M. Starr, *Executive Decisions and Operations Research*, in essentially the same form as here, has received attention unexpected by us. See *The New Yorker*, July 21, 1962, p. 68 and Jacques Barzun, *Science: The Glorious Entertainment* (New York: Harper & Row, 1964), p. 176.

jective, people customarily maintain various objectives. Each is relevant to some phase of their life activities.

2. Multiple objectives are frequently in conflict with each other, and when they are a *suboptimization* problem exists.

3. A particularly important aspect of the suboptimization problem is temporal. This means that (at best) we can only optimize as of that time when the decision is made. This will frequently produce a suboptimization when viewed in subsequent times.

4. Typically, decision problems are so complex that any attempt to discover *the* set of optimal actions is useless. Instead, people set their goals in terms of outcomes that are *good enough* (Simon's principle of bounded rationality).

5. Granted all the difficulties, human beings make every effort to be rational in resolving their decision problems. To help, they have a great store of past human experience codified for them in the form of ethical principles. These principles, maxims, and heuristics are such, that adhering to them is no guarantee of success—but they do afford guidance.

ORGANIZATIONAL OBJECTIVES

When we consider organizational objectives we find difficulties and solutions that are not unlike those of an individual. An organization certainly differs from an individual with regard to procedures for achieving rationality, the nature of suboptimization, as well as the ethics that may help to guide it. Nevertheless, the organization's problems of formulating objectives are essentially the same as those of the individual.

First, what is an organization? Most business organizations take the form of corporations, which are equivalent to legally created persons. But these fictitious persons are markedly different from real persons in several major respects. They have no appointed number of years and for all practical purposes can be considered to be eternal. The same applies to governmental organizations and other institutions.

Obviously, qualities such as happiness have no relationship to such organizations. Nonetheless, the importance of having basic overriding organizational objectives, as well as the impossibility of formulating a single objective to cover all cases, is clear. Probably the best move is to affirm the fundamental assumption of accounting: that the organization is a going, continuing, and surviving entity. Phrased in terms of this fundamental objective, every organization strives to survive, to maintain its existence, and to grow.[4]

For the individual, the analog to this organizational objective would be the continuity of his life. But survival is not the all-important objective of most individuals, even though it is a singularly important subobjective. This is demonstrated by the historical fact that literally millions of individuals have given their lives (however reluctantly or cheerfully) for the sake of values and objectives that they held dear. This point should give us pause in the case of organizations. Perhaps they, too, have more deeply held objectives than simply continuing their existence.

Fortunately, we do not have to analyze this question. Both organizations and individuals are likely to find that the search for one underlying objective is fruitless. Even if the survival objective were accepted, it would provide little help in solving decision problems. The question would still remain: What state of affairs ensures a continued existence? The problem of suboptimization over time would be but one of many which would arise to haunt the administrators. For organizations, as for individuals, we find that the maintenance of multiple objectives is a practical necessity, and consequently, an analytical requirement.

MULTIPLE OBJECTIVES

As in the case of the individual, the organization will maintain objectives in the different areas of its activities. Peter Drucker lists eight such categories:

> Market standing, innovation, productivity, physical and financial resources, profitability, manager performance and development, worker performance and attitude, public responsibility.[5]

A specific organizational entity can ignore any one of these areas—but only at the risk of its future performance in the others. As soon as we recognize the existence of multiple objectives we are faced with the

---

[4] Even in those cases where growth is rejected as an objective, evidence indicates that this disclaimer is invalid. Whether it be growth in power or in size, Parkinsonian influences are evident. Parkinson states, "Work expands so as to fill the time available for its completion." (*Parkinson's Law,* by C. Northcote Parkinson, Boston: Houghton-Mifflin Company, 1957.)

[5] Peter Drucker, *The Practice of Management* (New York: Harper & Brothers, 1954), p. 63.

problems of suboptimization. How does this work out in the case of the business organization? Let us follow Peter Drucker in his discussion of what may happen if a business devotes its attention exclusively to profit.

> To obtain profit today they tend to undermine the future. They may push the most easily saleable product lines and slight those that are the market of tomorrow. They tend to short-change research, promotion, and the other postponable investments. Above all, they shy away from any capital expenditures that may increase the invested-capital base against which profits are measured; and the result is dangerous obsolescence of equipment. In other words, they are directed into the worst practices of management.[6]

Any one of the objectives, emphasized to the exclusion of the rest, can lead to equally unpleasant consequences.

ORGANIZATIONAL PROBLEMS OF SUBOPTIMIZATION

Under what conditions does suboptimization arise? We can answer that it may arise whenever an action has the effect of improving the outcomes for some objectives while simultaneously impairing the outcomes for others. If the performance of one part of a system (a subsystem) is improved and this results in an impairment of the total system's performance, we have clear evidence of suboptimization. The best course of action in any specific decision problem is to utilize intuition, experience, and all available methodology to determine whether actions intended for one purpose are likely to have detrimental effects on other objectives. Ultimately, we wish to know how the overall performance of the system has fared. When the objectives cannot be measured on the same scale, it is exceedingly difficult to know what to do. All problems that involve conflicting objectives must be approached with full awareness of this fact.

It should be noted that a most serious problem exists when it is not possible to express all of the different (but relevant) outcomes in terms of a single *utility* measure. Fortunately, many organizations' decision problems can be framed in terms of dollars. Clearly, however, it is by no means the case that *all* organizational objectives can be expressed in monetary terms. If, to take an instance, employees' attitudes could be measured in dollars, then all outcomes derived from their attitudes

---

[6] Drucker, *The Practice of Management,* p. 62.

could be expressed in dollars. The overall objective could then be stated as the maximization of profit. We would not require a special (nondollar) description of employee morale, satisfaction, and general attitude. But no such easy solution to our problem exists. All problems of conflicting objectives pose difficult situations. We do, however, have some procedures for dealing with such problems.[7]

Looking at the bright side, there are many important decision problems that involve objectives which are measurable on a single scale. For these we can optimize the total system's outcome without fear of producing a serious suboptimization. At the minimum, an organization should attempt to optimize its situation with regard to each of its specific objectives—as long as it does not affect adversely its other objectives. This construction is a variant of an idea introduced (in a somewhat different context) by the Italian economist and sociologist, Vilfredo Pareto.[8]

Pareto was concerned with the problem of what principles should govern the actions of society if it is assumed that the utilities of the individuals composing the society cannot be compared. By *utility* we mean the subjective value that each individual subscribes to the various goods and services available. Under these circumstances society cannot act to achieve the greatest total utility because each individual's utility is unlike that of his neighbor. *Pareto suggested that society should try to achieve a condition such that each individual had the maximum utility possible without subtracting anything from anyone else's utility.* In other words, if society can act so as to increase one individual's utility without taking anything away from anyone else, then it should do so. A condition where this has been accomplished is known as *Paretian optimality.*

The Pareto problem arises because there is no common standard or measure of value between individuals. And this is analogous to the problem of multiple objectives with which we are dealing. Our problem exists because there is no uniform and universal measure of value for the various objectives. If there were one common measure (or dimension) we could formulate a single objective rather than several. Therefore we can state (with Pareto) that organizations should at least attempt to achieve a condition of Paretian optimality with regard to their various objectives.

---

[7] See, for example, David W. Miller and Martin K. Starr, *Executive Decisions and Operations Research* (Englewood Cliffs, N.J.: Prentice-Hall, Inc., 1960), pp. 161-65.

[8] Born in Italy, 1848.

We have seen how the problem of temporal suboptimization arises for individuals. This is obviously also true of organizations and precisely for the same reason: the very limited ability to foretell the future. It must be emphasized that although the ability to forecast is limited, it is, nevertheless, existent. The decision to build a new factory requires knowledge of future sales, economic trends, costs of land and of building, and so on. The location chosen, the design of the building, the dates of construction, and many other factors taken together represent the opportunity to optimize if we could only predict the future. However, with imperfect predictions we must suboptimize. Similar statements can be made for hospitals, universities, libraries, theaters, thruways, and reservoirs.

Let us consider another illustration. Many companies manufacture products that are on the drawing boards years in advance. As much as possible, they would like to reserve judgment on design commitments that would inexorably fix the nature of the product. To the greatest extent that it is feasible, decisions are made that permit a broad range of eventualities. In this way, the degree of suboptimization can be improved over time, thereby permitting a gradual approach to an overall optimum. The same reasoning applies to short- and long-range organizational planning. If a short-range planning decision does not permit sufficient eventualities to emerge in the long-range plan, then it creates a static suboptimization, which cannot be improved upon.

Business organizations are subject to still another kind of suboptimization problem. Whereas a real person is an entity that cannot be segmented, the *fictitious person* of the business corporation is usually made up of a number of departments, divisions, and branches. The successful functioning of the business demands the integration of the efforts of the various units that compose it. The achievement of enterprise objectives is based on the way that the various departments, divisions, and branches achieve their own objectives. By the very nature of things, the segments are likely to have considerable autonomy, and it can happen that the objectives they set are not in accord with the overall objectives of the organization. The actions of one department may have an effect on other departments. An optimal strategy for one division (in terms of its own objectives) can deleteriously affect other departments and, hence, the entire enterprise. Both of these situations represent typical variants of the suboptimization problem.

Examples of these problems are legion. Lack of accord of objectives is a major organizational problem. For example, an administrator, on doctor's orders, may accept a newly imposed objective of peace, quiet, and the avoidance of stress. This could easily be very much out of phase with the firm's objectives. A salesman's objective of maximizing his income may be in poor accord with the company's desired product mix or with the (long-term profit) requirement to devote time and attention to prospective customers. At yet another level, a research department can devote 90 per cent of its time to short-range projects so that its record of immediate achievement is impressive. This may be perfectly all right, but what happens if the competition does not have a similarly short-range point of view? Ultimately, the research department's short-term emphasis will cause extreme hardships for its own organization.

Suboptimization problems are very common and can be significantly harmful. We consider it worthwhile to present a more detailed example of how this kind of situation occurs. The example that we shall describe will illustrate a lack of organizational accord with respect to inventory policy objectives.

Assume that a leading chemical manufacturer has ten plants located at different places in the country. Four of the plants are large, four are of medium size, and two are small. Each plant requires many thousands of different spare parts. A supply of parts is stored at a warehouse adjacent to each plant. Management decides that the capital investment in spare parts is large enough to warrant doing a methodological analysis of inventories. Their objective is to minimize the total cost of inventory by taking into account the costs associated with carrying inventory and the penalties for being out of stock.

In the course of the analysis each plant manager is asked to specify how often each part can be allowed to go out of stock, i.e., one time out of ten demands, one in a hundred, one in a thousand.[9] The allowable outage rate is sometimes called the *alpha-level*. The plant managers do their best to group all spare parts into alpha-level classes. Some parts are assigned an alpha-level of 0.001, others 0.01, and so on. The criterion the manager uses in assigning parts to alpha-classes is the importance of the part to his operations as contrasted with the cost of stocking the part. A part that is costly to carry, and which is not crucial to maintaining production, would be assigned a high alpha-level, such as 0.5 or even 1.0. (The value of 1.0 would mean that the part was never kept in stock and was always obtained as needed.)

---

[9] He might prefer to specify allowable outages per time period, e.g., once in a year, once in five years, etc. This can be converted to allowable outages per demand. The manager seldom has any conclusive way to assign these designations, but he usually does have an intuitive feel about them.

We can assume that the plant managers will rate all parts that are in common use in about the same way. It will then fall upon central management to introduce differences in the alpha-level estimates based on the relative importances of the various plants to the enterprise. The alpha-level represents the permissible frequency with which parts can be out of stock. But, the loss of goodwill and/or production that results from an "out-of-stock" in a small plant will usually be less costly to the enterprise than would be the case for one of the large plants. For example, central management might say: Our large plants are four times more important to us than our small plants. Consequently, large-plant customers account for more of our dollar volume than customers of small plants. Also, to shut down the production unit of a large plant—because of a spare part outage—would reduce output far more than a similar small-plant outage. Therefore, we might adjust the small-plant alpha-levels, say by multiplying them by four. This serves to increase the permissible frequency for small-plant outages.

Now, what does this mean to the small-plant manager? It means that he will be out of stock four times more frequently than the manager of the large plants. Is he not justified in asking: Will central management always remember why *I* am out of stock more often than the large plants? Will top management forget the underlying reasons and use my repeated outages to reinforce their belief in the greater competence of large-plant managers? Will this system spoil my chances of becoming a large-plant manager? After considerable soul-searching the small-plant manager finds an answer that satisfies his conscience as well as his desire to look as good as the next fellow. He decides to inflate his forecasts of demand. In other words, he protects himself from going out of stock more often than the others by indicating greater demands than he actually expects. When the alpha-level modified by central management is applied to this *inflated figure* the result may be that the manager of the small plant will go out of stock even less frequently than the manager of the large plant. Within his own organization he is certainly more respected than would be the case if he had to explain to the sales department and to his production men why they must go out of stock so often.

Let us consider further why the managers rated their respective alpha-levels in the same way while central management did not think that this was so. Was central management wrong? No, central management was attempting to estimate the relative penalties to the enterprise as a whole for being out of stock at each location. To accomplish this it was necessary to adjust the managers' estimates. On the basis of company-wide information they were in a position to do this, whereas the managers were too localized to have the necessary perspective. The only way that the managers could have derived the same results as central management would have been if they knew the actual cost to the *integrated company* of being out of stock at each location. Without enterprise data no one plant manager could succeed in correctly characterizing the total system. The cost of carrying stock will not be identical for each location, but it is likely to be nearly the same. On the other hand, the out-of-stock cost will differ markedly, depending on the amount of goodwill sacrificed by not filling an order and the size of the production unit that might have to close down if a single part is missing. Specifically, the out-of-stock cost of the large plant is likely to be much larger than that of the small plant. Common sense suggests, and analysis verifies, that this means that the large plant should be out of stock less often than the small plant. Central management designs the alpha-levels to reflect this fact and approximates the optimal solution by weighting the alpha-levels according to the relative importance of each plant.[10] Generally the individual plants would not be able to do this. However, even if they were able, the small-plant manager would hardly be reconciled to the fact that he would lose more customers than his colleagues.

At the expense of a digression, we have gone into this inventory situation in some detail. It is a clear-cut case of an organization attempting to optimize across all of its components. Enterprise optimization is achieved to the disadvantage of the small plant. It is only natural that the small-plant manager would try to conceive of a strategy to offset the loss he would otherwise have to take. The small-plant manager's strategy is to optimize his own position and his plant's position first. The result of this conflict of objectives is suboptimization.

We have illustrated how suboptimization can occur between one part of an organization and the overall organization. Let us now consider suboptimization where two parts of a company are in conflict with each other. For example, a division's objective of achieving the best possible profitability record may lead it to purchase parts from competitors rather than from another division of the same company. This may lower the profitability of the division that normally supplies these parts. As another aspect of the inventory problem, a sales manager's objective of maximizing sales may lead him to want a large inventory

---

[10] Note that it is assumed here that the true costs of being out of stock are not known, as is often the case in practice.

so that all orders can be promptly filled. This is likely to be in conflict with the controller's objective of tying up a minimum of capital in inventory. Which one of these objectives is in the best interests of the business? As a final example, a production manager may decide to use less steel by reducing the upper tolerance limit of a machined part. The foreman provides a new machine setting. This results in a greater number of pieces that are too short. The rejects are discovered at the final assembly. Eventually, having lost track of the original causes, a complete redesign of the product may be required with no appreciable gains in cost or quality.

These examples serve to demonstrate the crucial importance of the suboptimization problem. Being aware of the situation, we must rely on uncommonly good common sense to help us to discover which way to proceed. Fortunately, many suboptimization problems are not totally intractable. They can at least be approached by new methods and deeper understanding of organization and systems theory. For example, the conflicting interests of the sales manager and the controller, with respect to inventory, can generally be resolved by expressing all relevant factors as costs measured in dollars. Then the decision problem can be solved in terms of a single, unified business objective, *viz.*, the minimization of costs.

This simple statement makes the difficult seem easy. To remove this illusion we need only recall the problems of the small-plant manager. How can we express the loss of dignity that he experiences as a result of being out of stock more often than he would like? Similarly, how do we represent the loss of customer goodwill that results from being unable to deliver an item that the customer wants immediately? How do we evaluate the lack of a hospital bed or the added value of each additional library book? Despite the enormous difficulties, sometimes these kinds of problems can be satisfactorily resolved.

BOUNDED RATIONALITY OF THE ORGANIZATION

Simon's idea of bounded rationality holds for organizations just as much as, and perhaps even more than, it does for individuals. First, suboptimization problems arise because the situational complexity forces boundaries to be placed on the size of the system to be studied. For many decision problems it is necessary to assume that the action taken in one department will have no significant effect on another department. Yet we know full well that an organizational entity is a functioning whole and that adjustments in one area will almost always have at least some effect on other areas of the enterprise. In spite of this, the assumption of independence is usually made, and successfully. Every factor cannot be considered in a problem precisely because of the limitations of human rationality.

Second, there are sharp constraints on the availability of information needed to resolve a decision problem. The cost of collecting, sorting, analyzing, and synthesizing information operates as an immediate constraint. It is said that many sales promotion and advertising problems would have better solutions if detailed information were available about the sales of competitors by regions. Since this information is rarely available with any degree of accuracy we have to do as well as we can without it. Laboratory experiments, test markets, and the like are specifically designed to overcome whatever handicaps follow from information scarcity.

Third, sometimes the reverse holds; there are enormous excesses of information that cannot be sorted, classified, and processed in any economic sense. We have Census tapes of demographic data, financial reports, Public Health data, Bureau of Labor statistics, stock market records, store audit reports, and piles of other kinds of information which (at the minimum) have some peripheral value. How does one go about squeezing out that value? Information inundation can be quite as debilitating as information scarcity. Consider, for example, the promotional problems of a large mail-order house. Such an organization typically will have huge masses of information in its files concerning the addresses of past customers, what they bought, how they made payment, and various other forms of data. Quite possibly, the accurate formulation of promotional decisions would benefit from the analysis of all this information. Yet even the assistance of large-scale computers may not prevail over the costs of programming and extracting meaningful summary data in useful form for the human user bounded in his rationality. Even if data collection and its processing were free, who would have the time to study the many thousands of results? It is understandable that most frequently we settle for small bits and sampled pieces of the total available information. This we blend with informed judgment, some belief in ourselves, and a sanguine hope for the best.

Fourth, there are usually an incredibly large number of possible states of nature, to say nothing of competitive actions. No decision problem could begin to be formulated if the attempt were made to include all of these possibilities. Almost any change in the economy, or in national and international affairs, influences the future behavior of the enterprise. Perturbations such as these mean that the search for an optimum solution of any specific decision problem ultimately must yield a less than optimal result because some of the critical factors are not taken into account.

Therefore, the organization is as realistic as the individual decision-maker. It is not likely to direct its administrators to strive for an optimum in the total sense. Instead, a group of situations that are good enough will be selected and satisfaction will be realized when a reasonable suboptimization is obtained. In other words, the organization will attempt to minimize the opportunity costs of the enterprise within the framework of the bounded rationality of the executive council.

PRINCIPLES AND POLICIES

Fortunately, the organization (just like individuals coping with their personal problems) has a vast store of knowledge available. This knowledge has been abstracted by the members of the management team from the experiences of their innumerable predecessors. These generalizations and rules of thumb function for the organization in the same way that ethical principles serve the individual. And, similarly, these are not laws that can be disproved by a contrary instance. Rather, they are means of calling attention to aspects of the decision situation that might be overlooked and to risks that might otherwise pass unnoticed.

Consider, for example, the policy that the current liquid assets should be at least equal to the current liabilities. This policy is not invalidated because some particular corporation can be shown to have ignored it yet to have achieved success and affluence. The policy simply codifies the fact that many organizations *have run into difficulties* because they ignored this ratio. Another example is the frequently stated policy of large department stores: "The customer is always right." Do they really think that this is true? Far from it. Do they always act as if it were true? Certainly not. It serves, however, to alert the clerks and department managers to the fact that the objectives of the store demand careful attention to customer relations.

In short, it is the exceptions that must be justified, not the principles or policies that traditionally guide the organization's administration.

SUMMARY OF THE GOAL-SEEKING CHARACTERISTICS
OF ORGANIZATIONS

We can summarize the important aspects of organizational objectives that we have considered as follows:

1. Organizational goals cannot be described by one simple objective, but rather with multiple objectives.
2. Multiple objectives are required to understand the organization's relationship with the outside world. Conflicts between these objectives lead to one type of organizational suboptimization.
3. Multiple objectives also exist within the organization. The fictitious entity, which is the organization, is built of many groups and subgroups which are in themselves entities. The individual is the basic building bloc of the structure. Conflicts of two basic kinds occur, but it is quite clear that many variations can appear. Conflicts between the organization and any lesser group are one cause of suboptimization. Conflicts between components of the organization also result in suboptimization.
4. As was the case for the individual, suboptimization occurs in time. The relationship of short-range to long-range planning requires that short-range planning should not destroy the flexibility of the long-range plan. Short-range planning is certainly suboptimization, but it is decision-making in a framework that is expected to include the opportunity for optimization. Moving in steps, the suboptimization approaches optimization in the long run.
5. Organizational decision problems are admittedly very complex. But organizational objectives do not have the entirely tenuous nature of many individual objectives. Frequently it is possible to find measurable quantities that represent utility to the organization. The discovery of "true" optimality is no more available to the organization than it is to the individual; nevertheless, it is frequently possible to determine a suitable or allowable degree of suboptimization.
6. The administrators of organizations make every effort to be rational in their decisions. They are, of course, affected by bounded rationality as are all individuals. However, they have a vast body of past experience, part of which is codified in the form of policy, to guide them.

Despite difficulties, we all know that managers strive valiantly to achieve rational decisions. No amount of emphasis on the difficulties should ever be permitted to obscure this fact. Creativity, intuition, know-how, experience—all these play their role in the decision process. But the creative burst of insight precedes, it doesn't replace, the rational part of the decision-making process. To convince others, to evaluate between two different creative insights, to subject the creative insight to the cold light of reason—all these require the weighing and evaluating of alternative strategies in terms of the objectives, the possible states of nature, and the competitive strategies. In other words, the rational decision-making process is called into play. We now turn, in the next chapter, to a consideration of how decision problems can be formulated in a manner that permits a rational approach to their solution.

PROBLEMS

1. What would be the teleological explanation of a severe drop in sales? What would be the positivistic explanation? How would an "open systems" analyst view the loss in sales?

2. Considering the example of the mail-order company, Table 3.1 and Figure 3.1, assume that new customers are obtained in an oscillating pattern as follows: 6, 8, 10, 8, 6, 4, 2, 4, 6, 8, 10, 8, 6, 4, 2, 4, 6, 8, ... Draw the graph of total orders when the repeat-order rate is: First week, $\frac{1}{2}$; second week, $\frac{1}{4}$; third week, $\frac{1}{8}$; . . . . If management can control repeat-order rates, what values should they establish in order to smooth the curve of total orders? (Notice the effect of allowing no reorders in the first, second, and third weeks.)

3. A manager of a supermarket wants to set up a test to determine how to make each aisle section yield optimal profit. In what way is the manager suboptimizing? How serious is the mistake? How can suboptimization between aisle sections be avoided?

4. Two products are manufactured on the same equipment. A decision is to be made concerning the proportion of each product that will be manufactured. Why is this not a genuine suboptimization problem? It is then learned that the wife of the president of the company favors one product over another. Why has the problem now become a real suboptimization situation?

5. The cost of carrying a unit of stock, for a period of time is called C_1. It is frequently determined by applying the interest rate that can be obtained

on capital to the cost of the item plus the cost of storage, insurance, and so on. For example, $\frac{1}{2}$ of 1 per cent, or 0.005 (a yearly interest of 6 per cent), is multiplied by the combined costs of the item, if C_1 is to be determined on a monthly basis. Therefore, an item with total costs of $100 has a C_1 of $0.50.

Use the 6 per cent interest rate to estimate the carrying costs, C_1. Also estimate the out-of-stock cost per unit for a period of time, called C_2, for the situations described below. Then determine the alpha-level that might apply for each of them, where alpha-level $= \dfrac{C_1}{C_1 + C_2}$.

    a. A new-car salesman.

    b. A used-car salesman.

    c. An airplane manufacturer.

    d. A kite manufacturer.

6. Assume that the ordering quantity specified by the inventory plan of a chemical manufacturer is given by the following formula:

$$Q = x + \frac{10(1 - 2\alpha)\sqrt{x}}{3}$$

where Q = reorder quantity (number of units),
    x = forecasted demand for a specified period, and
    α = alpha-level.

For a particular part, the small-plant manager is given an alpha-level of 0.20. For the same part, the large-plant manager is given an alpha-level of 0.02. By how much will the small-plant manager increase his reorder quantity in order to have the same alpha-level as the large plant? (Give the answer in terms of x.)

7. The sales manager of a tire manufacturer reported to the President that, on the basis of a statistical analysis just completed, the next year's dollar volume had been predicted to reach $40 million. The President said, "I'm not interested in your projections. Next year you will do $55 million of business. That's our objective and I expect you to achieve it." What does this dialogue mean? Whose approach do you subscribe to and why?

8. Frederick W. Taylor is called by many "the Father of Scientific Management" (Note: not Management Science, which traces its course from the 1940s). Taylor painstakingly studied bricklaying and prescribed in a step-by-step fashion the best way he could conceive of performing this activity. Later, time and motion analysts, belonging to the same school of thought, applied Taylor's approach to improve the productivity of many jobs. Yet inherent in these studies was the ever-present threat of serious

suboptimization. Can you explain why this is so and, additionally, what might be done to alleviate this problem?

9. Is a heat-sensing, guided missile an example of an open or closed system? Explain. How about an amoeba?

10. An employee of an automobile company owns 300 shares of common stock of that company. For the past five years he has been receiving $0.90 of dividends per share. The union of which he is a member has been pressing the company for wage increases, which in his case would amount to $250 per year. Management of the company claims that the wage hike would necessitate cutting the dividend in half. This would of course decrease the value of the stock which is presently yielding 4%. Formulating reasonable estimates, how might this employee vote at a union meeting to determine whether or not to demand the wage increase? What type of problem is this? Discuss.

11. You have been asked to prepare a plan for diversification which employs as much sequential decision flexibility as possible. Explain what is expected of you, why it is desirable, and how you intend to go about achieving this objective.

12. When you choose a vacation you have multiple objectives in mind. List the most important of these and explain how *you* go about resolving the conflicts that ensue from attempting to maximize the total utility of your decision.

PART II

THE
THEORY
OF
DECISIONS

4

The Structure of Decisions

Chapter 2 explained the necessity for some measure of the degree to which an objective is achieved. And in that chapter we noted that some objectives seem to permit only two possibilities: either they are achieved or they are not. Other objectives have a natural measure of the degree to which they are achieved—for example, the amount of profit. And there are still other objectives that seem to have degrees of achievement, but for which there appears to be no straightforward way to measure this degree.

For rational decision-making, we require some kind of measurement. As much as possible, our decision theory will be based on numbers and not on words. Even when numbers seem to be available as a natural consequence of a process, it cannot be taken for granted that they are the right numbers. Therefore, we must investigate in detail the means at our disposal for measuring the degree of attainment of an objective.

DEVELOPMENT OF THE PAYOFF MEASURE

In our formulation of the decision problem we have suggested that the manager has various possible *strategies* available to him; that he has one or more *objectives* which he is trying to achieve; and that a *state of nature* will occur which, together with the strategy he selected, will determine the degree to which he actually achieves his objective.

Another way of saying this is that the manager's selection of a strategy and the occurrence of a specific state of nature will result in a certain outcome. This outcome will yield some specific utility in terms of the manager's objectives. What we need is a measure of this utility and it is called, appropriately, a payoff measure.

In dealing with the idea of utility, and its measurement, we are by no means developing a new concept. It was previously mentioned that economists have long concerned themselves with these notions. However, the interest in measuring utility that resulted from various decision-theory applications has led to some new approaches to the problem. We don't need to discuss all of the developments concerning the measurement of utility, but we will need to treat some of them as we proceed.

The first point of importance is that utility must be defined in *subjective* terms. It is the utility of some specific individual or organization, not a common utility held by everyone. This results in problems that concern the comparison of the utilities of different individuals. Various aspects of this problem have led to many developments in economic theory, but for our purpose it is sufficient to note that the problem as stated is not solvable. There is no way to compare the utilities of different individuals.

It is worth emphasizing that utility is *defined* in subjective terms. Could it be that the inability to compare the utilities of two different individuals is simply a matter of definition? This is debatable, but in any case we will accept the current consensus that it is impossible to make such comparisons. The impossibility creates no unresolvable problems for decision theory as long as we are concerned with non-competitive situations, i.e., there are only states of nature at work. However, as soon as we become involved in decision problems where competitive actions are part of the situation we find that the impossibility of comparing utilities of different individuals has some important consequences.

Our second point of importance requires some development. The essence of the matter is that even for those objectives which seem to have a natural measure (profit, for example) it does not follow that the *obvious* measure is a measure of the utility to the decision-maker. In other words, the state of affairs of the decision-maker that finally results (when evaluated in terms of the objective) may have an entirely different utility measure than the natural measure would indicate. This can be readily illustrated.

Suppose someone offers to gamble with you on the following terms:

a coin will be tossed; if it comes up heads you will be paid $200, if it comes up tails you must pay only $100. Now, surely, this is an excellent arrangement for you. We might even suspect the sanity of the man who offered you such terms. However, the question is: Would you always accept the offer? It is clear that the amounts of money involved are distinctly in your favor. Half of the time you will win and thereby receive $200 increments. The other half of the time, you will lose, but only $100 increments.

In terms of utility, the question must be phrased: Is the utility that I sacrifice when I lose less than, equal to, or more than the utility I gain when I win? And, as a little thought quickly discloses, this varies with your circumstances. If you have a sufficient sum of money so that the loss of $100 doesn't destroy your financial situation you will probably find that the gain in utility when you win is greater than the loss in utility when you lose. (We will call this the first case.) Under these circumstances you would probably be happy to indulge in this particular gamble as often as your opponent would agree. But suppose, to take an extreme, that the total amount you have is $100 and you need this money to pay for transportation to the location of a new job which has been offered to you. (We will call this the second case.) Under these circumstances you might well feel that the loss of utility which would occur if you lost would be far greater than the gain in utility which would occur if you won.

Now, this little example is a genuine decision problem. To gamble or not to gamble are the two strategies that are available; to win or to lose are the two states of nature that can occur; and the objective is—what? Is it to maximize your total dollars? It appears that we cannot say this because it wouldn't cover the second case. Of course, we could say that this was the objective in the first case and something different was the objective in the second case. But it is certainly more convenient to formulate one objective that will cover either case, and that is easy to do. *The objective in either case is to maximize utility.* Apart from being an elementary decision problem, this example shows that the utility of dollars is not necessarily the same as the number of dollars.

BERNOULLIAN UTILITY

The question remains: What is the utility of a dollar and how can we measure it? A famous Swiss mathematician and philosopher, Daniel Bernoulli, had already treated this question in a paper he wrote circa 1730.[1] Bernoulli did not approach this problem empirically, i.e., by measuring the utilities of different individuals for money. In common with most thinkers of his time, he was philosophically a rationalist. This means he assumed that all men, being rational, would behave in the same way under similar circumstances. Bernoulli believed that all he had to do was deduce the fundamental laws which would govern such rational behavior. Bernoulli's argument led him to the specific conclusion that the utility of dollars (or francs, pounds, etc.) could be measured to a sufficiently good approximation by using the logarithm of the number of dollars as the measure of utility.

There is nothing sacrosanct about the selection of the logarithm as the measure of utility. Contemporaries of Bernoulli, who were equally rationalistic, reached some different conclusions. For example, Buffon, the famous French naturalist, concluded that the utility for money could best be represented by the reciprocal of the number of dollars;[2] a Swiss mathematician named Cramer opted for the square root of the number of dollars as the most satisfactory measure of utility. The basic approach in each case was the same. Certain "principles" are stated which seem to the author of the argument to be essential components of the approach of any rational man. From these principles a mathematical relationship is then deduced, which is intended to relate the utility for an amount of money and the amount of money itself. Bernoulli hypothesized that the utility of additional sums of money to an individual must be inversely proportional to the amount of money he already has. It follows that the more money one has, the less the utility of an additional amount. Buffon's and Cramer's alternatives are in accord with the basic proposition of diminishing utility—but not with Bernoulli's specific hypothesis. And hence the different conclusions that are reached.

In contrast to this somewhat old-fashioned, but not necessarily false, approach of the rationalists is the contemporary empirical attack on the problem. As empiricists we assume that utilities, being subjective, can differ, despite an identical set of external circumstances. Therefore, it behooves us to discover means for measuring the

---

[1] The Latin title was "Specimen Theoriae Novae de Mensura Sortis." The date is vague because the journal in which the paper appeared had one volume for the years 1730 and 1731, and this volume was not published until 1738.

[2] That is, if you have x dollars and you gain y dollars more, your increase in utility is proportional to $\frac{1}{x} - \frac{1}{x+y}$.

actual utilities of a given decision-maker. Various methods have been developed; and we shall discuss some of them shortly.

First, however, let us emphasize the possibility that the logarithm (or a similar measure) of the amount of dollars might be a correct measure of utility (or payoff) under certain circumstances. The same can also be said for the actual amount of dollars itself. We reiterate the important fact that even where the degree of achievement of objectives seems to be measurable in dollars, it may not be so. The same decision problem presented to several individuals may have different solutions, each being completely rational. Why is this so? Because the utility that different individuals place on a given sum of money will vary.

To illustrate this fact we can use the same problem with which Bernoulli was concerned, *viz*, the problem of self-insurance. But before we do this it will be necessary to introduce some elementary concepts of probability theory. These concepts play a most important role in decision theory, operations research, management science, and many other areas. We need only some of the ideas of the probability theory, and it will be simplest to introduce them piecemeal, as they are required.

PROBABILITY THEORY

Probability theory deals with events of a special kind, called *random events*. These are events for which the outcome is affected by chance. Frequently this situation occurs when an enormous number of causes contribute to produce the final outcome, which is the event in question. A typical example is tossing a coin. Whether it lands heads or tails is a chance event because such a large number of causes contribute to the final outcome. Such factors as the force with which the coin is tossed, the amount of spin, air movements, position of the hand when the coin is caught, all act together to determine the outcome. Probability theory deals with the conclusions that can be drawn in reasoning about such events. The basic concept is that of the *probability of the outcome*. The probability of an outcome can be most simply understood as the percentage of the times in which this outcome would occur if the event were repeated a great many times. Thus, we say that the probability of the outcome of (the event) heads in tossing a coin is $\frac{1}{2}$ because a great number of tosses will produce about 50 per cent heads. Similarly, the probability of rolling a 7 with two dice is $\frac{1}{6}$ because a great many rolls will produce 7's about 16⅔ per cent of the time.

Actually, the situation is a good deal more complicated than the preceding paragraph would indicate. Probability theory is not an example of the kind of austere, settled structures of thought which seem to be represented by such subjects as mathematics, logic, mechanics, and so forth. Quite the contrary, probability theory is riddled with controversy and one of the major arguments concerns the meaning of the basic concept—the probability of an outcome.

A particularly crucial difference of opinion exists between the (so-called) objectivists and subjectivists. The objectivists (in a simplified sense) maintain that probabilities must relate to long-run frequencies of occurrence. For them, only events which can be repeated for a "long run" may be governed by probabilities. Thus, for the objectivist the fact that the appearance of a head in a coin toss has a probability of occurring of one-half is simply a shorthand way of saying that heads would be produced about half the time if the coin were tossed a great many times. The subjectivists (also in a simplified version) maintain that probabilities measure degrees of belief in the likelihood of occurrence of a given outcome. "Degrees of belief" can be roughly translated as estimates of the proportion of times that a given outcome would occur if some imaginable, but perhaps physically impossible, series of trials were performed. For the subjectivists a probability represents a subjective appraisal of the nature of reality, while for the objectivists a probability must be an actual, countable, observable fact. Therefore, a subjectivist can perfectly well talk about, say, the probability of war, while an objectivist would maintain that such a use of probabilities is meaningless, since the situation in question could never be examined with repeated trials.

As we shall see, this difference in conception between objectivists and subjectivists has some important consequences. In the case of coin tosses, however, the interpretations are essentially equivalent. The subjectivist would maintain that, in addition to the logic of the mechanics of coin tossing, many historical records exist of lengthy coin tosses. And since these showed that heads appeared about one-half the time, then this fact constitutes a major basis for the establishment of a rational degree of belief. Consequently, the subjectivist will be willing to interpret the probabilities in this case in the objectivist's sense.

It is essential to be clear about this notion of long-run frequency of occurrence. What, after all, could it mean to say that the probability of heads is ½, that the probability of a seven with two dice is ⅙, or that the probability of being dealt a perfect bridge hand (13 cards of the same suit) is 1/158,753,389,900? In any of these cases the outcome in question will either happen or not—there is no intermediate possibility. What information, then, does the associated probability really give us? Only the percentage of times the outcome will occur if the event is repeated a great number of times. Note that the coin may show tails the first try, again on the second try, and even, perhaps, for the first ten tries. But, in the long run, we can expect to find that we have gotten about 50 per cent heads. Similarly, one might deal 158,753,-389,900 bridge hands and never get a perfect hand, or one might conceivably get one on the very first deal. Probability theory tells us, however, that if we dealt an enormous number of bridge hands—say one bridge hand for every fundamental particle in the universe (2 times   15,747,724,136,275,002,577,605,653,961,181,555,468,044,717,914,-527,116,709,366,231,425,076,185,631,031,296, according to Sir Arthur S. Eddington)—we would find that we had gotten pretty nearly one perfect hand for every 158,753,389,900 deals.

All of the probability examples we have used above have been of the sort that can be calculated in advance. But this is incidental for our present point of view. Suppose we are told that the probability is $\frac{1}{10}$ that the average January temperature in New York City will be greater than 40°F. What does this mean? It means, first, that someone has gone over the New York City weather records and discovered that in the past, 1 out of 10 Januaries had an average temperature of more than 40°F. It means, second, that barring a climatological change (i.e., the process is stable), we can expect approximately the same proportion in the future. At least this is the best information we have concerning the proportion to be expected in the future. The only difference between this case and the earlier ones above is in the method of determining the probabilities, not their interpretation. If we didn't know how to calculate the probability of getting a 7 with one roll of two dice we could roll the dice a great many times and observe how often we got the 7. As a matter of fact, this is exactly how it was done, and with considerable accuracy, by gamblers before probability theory was developed in the seventeenth century.

Now, the most important use of probabilities for our present purpose is in terms of the factors that govern rational behavior when money (or, more generally, utility) is involved in chance situations. The classical gambling situation is typical. What reasoning governs a wager on the toss of a coin? Suppose the same wager is going to be repeated a great number of times. Then we know that about 50 per cent of the time the coin will show heads. This means that the gambler who bets on heads will win about 50 per cent of the time and his opponent will win about 50 per cent of the time. So, if the game is not to produce an advantage for one or the other player it is necessary that the amounts bet should be equal for the two players.

Suppose the coin is tossed 1000 times. We would expect that either player would win about 500 bets and lose about 500. If he wins as much as he loses on each bet he ought to come out approximately even. Thus, in this case, a fair game requires that the odds should be even—each player betting the same amount of money. It is the fact that the odds were not even that gave so much advantage to one of the players in the coin-tossing example given before. If that game had been played 1000 times, the player who received $200 when he won and who paid only $100 when he lost could have expected to win 500 times and receive $100,000 while losing 500 times and paying out only $50,000, with a net gain of $50,000.

The same considerations apply to any other probabilities. Suppose one is betting on a 7. If the dice are rolled 6000 times, we know that there should be about 1000 7's. Thus, the person betting on the 7 would win 1000 times and lose 5000 times. In order to have an even game it is clearly necessary that he should receive more when he wins than he pays when he loses. In fact, he must receive $5 when he wins for each $1 he pays when he loses in order for the game to be even. Thus, fair odds for this game would be 5 to 1. If the odds are larger than 5 to 1, then it is an advantage to bet on a 7. If the odds are smaller, then it is an advantage to bet against a 7.

EXPECTED VALUE

Much of this reasoning can be clarified by introducing one concept: *expected value*. This idea is not complex. Expected value is simply the old fashioned arithmetic average. We shall express it with mathematical symbols, using W's (W_1, W_2, and so forth) to represent the possible numerical outcomes, and p's (p_1, p_2, and so forth) to represent the probability that each of the W's will occur. Thus, for two possible outcomes, we have

$$\text{Expected value} = W_1 p_1 + W_2 p_2$$

where $p_1 + p_2 = 1$, since either W_1 or W_2 necessarily has to occur.

Generalizing to an indefinite number of outcomes, say n of them, we can write

$$\text{Expected value} = p_1W_1 + p_2W_2 + \ldots + p_iW_i + \ldots + p_nW_n$$

$$= \sum_{i=1}^{i=n} p_iW_i$$

where Σ ("sigma") is the symbol for the mathematical operation of summing. This symbol gives instructions to add up what comes after it —in our case all terms of the form, p_iW_i. The entries "$i = 1$" and "$i = n$" show how many terms are to be included in the sum, in our case all terms from p_1W_1 to p_nW_n inclusive.

The W's may be all positive or all negative, or some may be positive and some negative, depending on the problem. For example, consider the executive who is certain to get one or the other of two possible bonuses. Let W_1 be one of the bonuses and W_2 the other. Then if we know the probability of getting each bonus (i.e., we have p_1 and $p_2 = 1 - p_1$) we can write the equation representing the expected value of the executive's bonus. Here both of the bonuses are positive. This is, however, a matter of convention. We automatically think of income (in this case, the executive's bonus) as being positive and, hence, any outgo (such as taxes) as being negative. But we would reach no contradictory conclusion if the convention were reversed—as long as we remained consistent. Thus, when we analyze a problem in terms of costs it is not unusual to make costs positive. If this procedure is followed, then it is certainly necessary to make profits negative so that our analysis can balance out.

Frequently we will be using the expected value equation where one of two W's is positive, the other negative. This is the situation when there is the possibility of either a gain or a loss—the gambler's predicament. For example, what is the expected value of a coin toss upon which two players each bet $100? Here we can let W_1 represent the gain of $100 ($W_1$ is positive), and W_2 the loss of $100 ($W_2$ is negative). Then we have $100 ($\frac{1}{2}$) - $100($\frac{1}{2}$) = 0$ as the expected value. What is your advantage if the other player puts $200 against your $100? Simply $200($\frac{1}{2}$) - $100($\frac{1}{2}$) = 50. Under these conditions you should average $50 gain *on each play;* if you play 1000 times you should have $50,000 to show for it.

We are not limited to expected values of additions or subtractions such as rates of return, profits, gains, or losses. We can take the expected values of any quantities, of similar dimension, whatsoever. It is often useful to take directly the expected value of total capital. For example, assume you have a total capital of $500 and you are offered the coin toss of $200 against your $100. Then we can identify the W's with total capital. If you win you will have $700, and if you lose you will have $400. Therefore we have $700(\frac{1}{2}) + \$400(\frac{1}{2}) = \$550$, which is the expected value of your capital *after one toss*. Let us now consider how one might more broadly use this concept of expected value.

Suppose you have the choice of making two investments of $1000 each. Presume that the return on investment A will be $4\frac{1}{2}$ per cent and the return on investment B will be 6 per cent. Granted the certainty of these statements and assuming that you are motivated by the objective of getting the greatest possible return you will undoubtedly invest in B. This conclusion follows because your return from B will be $60 compared to only $45 return from A. But now suppose that you are informed that both of the investments are risky and that the risk is greater on investment B. Suppose, to be precise, that you are told that the probability of a return on investment A is 0.90 (90 per cent) and the probability of a return on B is 0.65 (65 per cent). We will assume that either you will get the full stated percentage return or else no return at all. How would you choose between the investments?

We can calculate the expected values for the two investments in accordance with our equation. Assume that the capital invested will remain secure in any event and the only question is whether there is a return or not. In this case the amounts won will be the return on the investment and the amounts lost will be 0—simply the fact of not receiving a return. Then, using our equation, the expected value for investment A will be $\$45(0.9) - 0(0.1) = \$40.50$. The expected value of investment B will be $\$60(0.65) - 0(0.35) = \$39$. This means that if we made a number of different investments identical in every respect to investment A we would expect an average return of $40.50 on each of them. For a number of investments similar to investment B we could expect an average return of only $39. We could, therefore, conclude that we should invest in A because our expected return from A is larger than it is from B.

Note that we said "could conclude" rather than "must conclude." The reasoning we followed is perfectly logical and affords complete justification for choosing investment A. However, we cannot deny that one might prefer to play a hunch and invest in B and that he might be right and we might be wrong in this specific instance. This in no way changes the fact that our reasoning is impeccable, granting the probabilities as given and the objective as stated. The same question arises concerning gambling. One person may play the odds correctly and lose, while another ignores them and wins. Perhaps it may be the case that some individuals have a sixth sense (but this is equivalent to saying that they have more information than we do). Those of us who don't have a sixth sense (or data-collector) can be consoled by the fact that most individuals who do think they have one and who therefore ignore the relevant probabilities eventually suffer the consequences.

In this reasoning concerning expected values we have bypassed the point with which we started—namely, that individuals do not have the same utility for money. We calculated above the considerable advantage accruing to the individual who receives $200 in the coin-tossing game for each $100 he wagers. Yet we have previously stated that under certain conditions (our so-called second case) we wouldn't accept this handsome offer. There is no contradiction. Instead of expected value we need only calculate the *expected utility*. Precisely the same procedure is used, except that we measure the utility of the amounts involved instead of the amounts themselves. This kind of calculation will be illustrated when we examine Bernoulli's problem of self-insurance.

SELF-INSURANCE

What is the problem of self-insurance? Individuals or organizations faced with the risk of loss of assets can either assume the risk themselves or pay an insurance company to assume the risk for them. The question is: When is it reasonable to do one or the other?

Let us take as an example a shipment of goods worth $10,000 that has a probability of 0.10 (10 per cent) of being destroyed or lost in transit. What is the expected value of such a shipment? Using our equation we have $10,000(0.90) + 0(0.10) = 9000, reflecting the fact that out of 100 shipments only 90 will arrive. Put in another way, the shipper can expect that on the average he will sustain a $1000 loss in value for each shipment. It would follow on this basis that the shipper should be prepared to pay *up to* $1000 for each shipment as premium on insurance. In this way, he will suffer no loss on his merchandise value. Instead he will pay some amount in premiums to the insurance company.

On the face of it, only if the cost of the premium is equal to or less than the expected cost of the loss in merchandise would the shipper insure. When the costs are equal we will call this break even. We may note, however, that the process is such that the shipper is going to lose money in either case. He would just like to minimize this loss. Thus, if the shipper paid $1000 for each shipment, then he would pay a total of $10,000 in premiums for ten shipments and this would be repaid him for the one that was lost or destroyed. Consequently, he would break even on his premium payments. The lower the premium, below $1000, the more advantageous it would be for the shipper to insure.

From the standpoint of the insurance company a premium of $1000 per shipment would only enable them to break even and, since they wish to generate a profit, they would demand a higher premium, say $1500. By our previous cost-balance criterion this premium (greater than $1000) would seem to be disadvantageous to the shipper. Viewed. in the same light as gambling games, if the shipper takes insurance at a $1500 premium, then he has a *negative* expected value. That is, he loses on each play (shipment). Yet, under exactly this kind of circumstance, people continually insure themselves against loss. Why? Are they all being irrational? Of course the answer is no. They are not.

The explanation resides in the fact that the parties to the insurance contract have different amounts of capital and different utilities for increments of it. There is diminishing utility for money (the more one has, the less an additional amount will contribute to utility). That the diminishing utility should be measured by the logarithm of the amount of money, as Bernoulli assumed, is not necessarily the case, but it will serve to illustrate the logic of the situation. Suppose the shipper has total assets of $15,000, including the shipment, which must arrive safely for the shipper to be paid. Then, according to Bernoulli's assumption of a logarithmic measure of utility, if he does not take insurance, the shipper will have utility equal to the logarithm of $15,000 or 4.17609 with probability of 0.90 and utility equal to the logarithm of $5000 or 3.69897 with probability of 0.10. His expected utility in this case is simply $4.17609(0.90) + 3.69897(0.10) = 4.12838$ (the utility of $13,439, since 4.12838 is the logarithm of $13,439). If he insures for a premium of $1500 he will always end up with $15,000 - $1500 = $13,500 and his utility will be the logarithm of $13,500 or 4.13033. Thus, the shipper's total expected utility is higher if he insures so this is the course of action he should take. This is so in spite of the fact that the cost of the premium is greater than the expected cost of the loss in merchandise.

From the standpoint of the insurance company it is rational to offer the insurance because the company has sufficient capital so that its total utility is increased by accepting the insurance. Assume that the insurance company has assets of only $100,000. If it doesn't accept the insurance its utility will be measured by the logarithm of $100,000 or 5. If it does accept the insurance it will have the utility of $101,500 or 5.00647 with probability of 0.90 and the utility of $91,500 or 4.96142 with probability of 0.10. Its expected utility if it accepts the insurance will therefore be 5.00647(0.90) + 4.96142(0.10) = 5.00196, the utility of $100,454. The insurance company should, therefore, accept the insurance for a premium of $1500. Thus, both parties are acting with complete rationality—once account is taken of the differences in the utility of money.

What, then, is the answer to the problem of whether to insure or not? It clearly depends on the amount of assets the shipper has. From the equation for his expected utility it can be calculated that he has equal utility whether he insures or not if his total assets are about $16,000. If he has more than this it is to his advantage to bear the risk himself. If he has less he should insure. Perhaps the shipper would scoff at the idea that with only $16,000 he should carry this risk himself. If so, it should be realized that this reflects the weakness of the logarithm, in this case, as a representation of the diminishing utility of money. If we had, for a specific shipper, the correct representation of his utility for money, we could use the same approach to determine at what point it was to his advantage to self-insure. Our use of the logarithm, we repeat, was only to illustrate the idea that it is utility that is important—not the amount of money.

The point of all this discussion is that even for objectives with a natural measure of degree of achievement it is still necessary to recognize that the natural measure may not coincide with the utility the decision-maker receives from the degree of achievement of his objective. And, if it doesn't, it is the *utility* that governs the decision problem, not the natural measure.

But there are many decision problems for which the amount of money involved does satisfactorily measure the utility. This would tend to be true where the amount of money involved is small relative to total assets. Can this be made more precise? Only if the real relation of the utility of additional increments of money to the amount of money possessed is known. For example, if the true relationship between utility and money is expressed by the logarithm of the amount of money, as Bernoulli suggested, then decision problems involving changes in money of no more than 2 to 3 per cent of the total amount possessed can be approximated with sufficient accuracy by assuming that the utility is represented by the amount of money. In short, the amounts of money involved could be used directly without worrying about the utility of the money. For decision problems involving greater proportions of total capital it would be necessary to determine the utility of the sums involved.

It is also important to note that problems arise as soon as a decision problem includes any risk of total loss, i.e., bankruptcy. The difficulty is indicated by the logarithm itself, since the log utility of zero is negative infinity. For some people, negative infinity, which is an infinite loss, would properly represent the situation. Other individuals, with suitable temperaments, don't look upon bankruptcy as the end of the road. For these people, it wouldn't be accurate to suppose that a small chance of complete failure would deter them. Obviously, personality and temperament differ widely at the zero end of the log scale.[3] Under these circumstances it is necessary to give careful consideration to each individual's measure of utility.

We have concerned ourselves so far only with objectives for which there exists a natural payoff measure of the degree of achievement. Even here we find difficulties, although they are not insuperable ones. Such natural measures exist for many organizational objectives. Since business is involved in economic activities one would expect to find that various economic indices would be relevant to many business objectives. Thus, we would expect that dollars would be a natural measure of payoff for objectives concerning profits and costs as long as the decision did not concern too great a percentage of the company's assets. Another kind of natural payoff measure is provided by brand share. In the same way, volume of sales, order size, number of customers, repeat order rate, public service levels and a large number of other payoff measures may be relevant to specific organizational objectives.

---

[3] If there is a 0.01 probability of bankruptcy we could represent this as (0.01) log $1.00. This would contribute zero utility, but subtract nothing from the utility obtained the remaining 99 per cent of the time. On the other hand, fractions of a dollar would subtract utility. One point of view is to take that fraction which subtracts as much utility as would be gained if bankruptcy did not result and apply the probabilities to these numbers. For example,

$$0.99 \log \$15{,}000 + 0.01 \log (1/\$15{,}000) = 0.99(4.17609) - 0.01(4.17609) = 4.09257$$

which is equivalent to $12,376.

Another point of view is to use as the measure of payoff a quantity called the probability of ruin. This is briefly discussed in Chapter 7.

PAYOFFS WITHOUT A NATURAL MEASURE

What happens when the objective is one of the many that have different degrees of achievement—and, hence, demand a payoff measure —but for which there is *no obvious measure* of payoff? Of the eight areas listed by Peter Drucker[4] that require objectives (discussed in Chapter 3) there are four that are clearly of this type: innovation, manager performance and development, worker performance and attitude, public responsibility. (Other objectives may fall in this category also.)

Let us consider an objective in the area of worker attitude. It might well be the achievement of satisfactory labor relations. Obviously, there are all manner of degrees and dimensions of labor relations. They range from high turnover, work stoppages and strikes, poor performance, and low morale to the case where everyone works until he reaches retirement, stoppages and strikes are unheard of, performance is excellent, and morale is tops. This example will serve to illustrate that it is possible to find some quantitative measures even for such an intractable objective as worker attitude. For instance, turnover rate, average length of service, or some index of productivity may be suitable for a payoff measure *in some cases*. But the difficulty is that usually no one of these seems to correspond to what the manager has in mind when he refers to satisfactory labor relations. If one of them is what he means, or some combination of several, then we need only try to discover whether there is a problem of determining the utility of various payoff measures. The more difficult case occurs when the manager isn't really sure what he means by satisfactory labor relations. He only knows that he will recognize them when he sees them.

This situation is not unfamiliar. Consider the problem of determining a quantitative measure of the state of health of an individual. There are an enormous number of quantitative measures involved in describing good health: blood sugar content, blood corpuscle count, weight, and the whole host of measures that doctors have occasion to use. For any one of them we can probably find limits such that it can be said that the individual won't be healthy unless this particular measurement lies between some specified limits. But the problem is that even if all the actual measures lie between their given limits the individual may still be unhealthy.

---

[4] Drucker, *The Practice of Management*, p. 63.

It is this fact that explains the need for the highly experienced diagnostician. If it were otherwise we could plug every individual's measurements into a computer and diagnose his condition from calculations performed on the total "model of health" with which the computer had been programmed. Work along this line is proceeding but it is very far from being anything but primitive. Meanwhile, wherever measurements are sufficient, doctors are quick to use them. Thus, since one of the major proofs of acute infectious mononucleosis is a change in the differential count of the white corpuscles, doctors have incorporated this knowledge as a major component in their diagnosis of this disease. And legitimately so, for such procedures give the doctor the opportunity to devote his experienced attention to other, more intangible evidence and to concern himself with the problem of the best treatment for the particular patient in question. The procedure is in accord with the development and use of knowledge. Some of the intangibles that one generation treats by experience are converted to measurable factors by the next generation. This process is a never-ending one because reality is far too complex to be completely circumscribed by a finite set of measurements.

In economics the same kind of problem is known as the *index number problem*. How, for example, can one achieve a quantitative measure that will describe the state of the economy? This case is extremely interesting because there are already available an extraordinarily large number of quantitative measures of different aspects of the economy. There is, quite literally, an embarrassment of riches. Part of the difficulty is due to the underlying notion that there must be a best state. But it is impossible to give satisfactory definition of what constitutes the best state. Certainly the majority of economists would recognize a good state when they saw it. There are a great number of possible relationships between all the measurable factors which would constitute a good-enough state. Perhaps this is one of the areas in which the principle of bounded rationality must operate. The question isn't really whether the national economy is optimal, only whether it is satisfactory.

So, recognizing that the problem we are dealing with is a general one, let us see what resources we have to deal with it. We can begin with a specific example. Suppose you are involved in contract negotiations with a union. You have, we will assume, the objective of achieving a satisfactory relationship with your workers. And, of course, you have a great number of possible strategies available to you in the form of specific offers and counteroffers to the union. Now, let us simplify the problem by assuming that there are only three possible relevant outcomes: strike, contract, or a continuation of the doubtful situation where negotiations proceed and the employees remain at work without a contract. It should be noted that under some circumstances it might be feasible to express these three possibilities in terms of dollar costs to the organization. If this were the case we could use the simpler methods discussed above, but we will assume that dollar costs cannot be determined.

RANKING

Now, the first possibility available to the administrator is that he can rank the possible outcomes in order of their utility to him. Ranking the outcomes simply means that they are put in the order of their utility, the most utility first, the least utility last. Thus, in our example, the executive may rank a contract first, continued negotiations second, and a strike third; in that order. Of course, this plausible ranking is by no means a necessary one. It all depends on the utility of each outcome to the decision-maker. For example, under some circumstances the administrator might rank a continuation of negotiations first because he anticipates a change in the economic situation which would improve his bargaining position. In any case, we are suggesting that only the administrator can rank the outcomes in order of their utility to *him* in terms of *his* objectives.

Can this always be done? Some things can't be ranked. One cannot, for example, rank cities of the world in accordance with their distance from the equator and from the international date line. One could rank them with either one of these distances separately, but not simultaneously. Similarly, an airplane's position cannot be ranked. That is, we cannot rank it unless our objective provides a criterion other than spatial position. In airport control, for example, planes are landed according to their altitude. The lowest plane in a stack is brought in first and all of the planes in the holding pattern are then lowered by one unit of altitude separation. The criterion is not to pass any plane through an altitude occupied by another plane. So we rank these airplanes by their order of arrival starting at one and counting up from the bottom. The position of a ship does not permit ranking; however, the rules of the road rank ships according to which ones have the right of way. We cannot rank color. But we can rank position of the dominant wave length in the visual spectrum. We can also rank purity and reflectance by wave length. Any given color can be defined in terms of three variables. By means of a suitable transformation, these can be reduced to two, but the ranking problem remains.

Mathematicians refer to this situation as a problem of *dimensionality*. A ranking implies only one dimension. It cannot be used on factors that have more than one dimension, as our examples had. The sense of taste is a phenomenon that has been shown to have more than one dimension. As a result, when psychologists devised taste tests in which the individual must rank his preferences for various tastes, it was found that he cannot always do it successfully. This shows up in the form of a breakdown of the transitivity of his preferences. *Transitivity* is a mathematical word signifying that if the individual prefers A to B, and prefers B to C, then he should not prefer C to A.

Transitivity holds as long as there is only one dimension. Examples of transitive relations are bigger, smaller, heavier, lighter, wealthier, healthier. Its breakdown in taste tests indicates the presence of more than one dimension of taste. Might this not happen when the manager attempts to rank his outcomes? It is tempting to answer no, because the manager will reach a decision implying that he has ranked his outcomes. However, this would be circular reasoning with a vengeance! The modicum of truth in this answer is that to make a decision the manager must *believe* that he has succeeded in ranking his outcomes. We leave open the possibility that upon various occasions he might not have been able to do so.

If the outcomes can be ranked, then the numerical ranks can be used as a measure of the utility of the outcome—the payoff. We shall find that rankings are sometimes sufficient for analyses of decision problems involving competitive actions. They can be useful also in analyzing decision problems involving states of nature. But they are not sufficiently informative to support an extensive analysis. The use of rankings of outcomes as measures of payoff is limited since the majority of arithmetical manipulations have no meaning in terms of ranks. For in our example, we cannot tell whether the difference in preferences between 1 and 2 is greater or less than the difference in preferences for 2 and 3. Averages of ranks, where (responding to the various states of nature) different outcomes can occur with one strategy, have no meaning. In short, while rankings are helpful—and must serve if nothing better is available—we cannot expect to be able to use any very sophisticated methods of analysis based on ranks.

It is worth investigating the arithmetical shortcomings of rankings a little more carefully. Take as an example the decision problem in labor relations mentioned above. Let us abbreviate the three alternatives by their initial letters: S for strike, C for contract, and N for negotiations. Our administrator has ranked these three outcomes in order: C, N, and S. Therefore, we assign these outcomes the ranks 1, 2, and 3, respectively. But we could equally well summarize the administrator's preferences with any other three numbers in the same order: say 1, 9, 28, or 7, 46, 259. The shortcomings become apparent when we recognize that the only arithmetical operations which can be performed legitimately on any one of these possible rankings[5] must be such that they would give an equivalent result when performed on any other of these rankings. For example, the 1, 2, 3 ranking would suggest that the difference in utility between C and N equaled the difference in utility between N and S. But this conclusion is completely contradicted by either of the other two rankings (1, 9, 28, or 7, 46, 259). Clearly, it is not legitimate to subtract numbers that represent ranks. Shortcomings such as this exist in the context of what we would like to be able to do. If the best measurements we can achieve are rankings then we use them regardless of our preferences.

We have seen that the arithmetical operation of subtraction is not legitimate when performed on numbers which represent rankings. This is because the answer obtained has no meaning for the outcomes being measured—utilities in our case. It can easily be verified that hardly any of the ordinary arithmetical operations can be performed on rankings. This includes addition, subtraction, multiplication, division, averaging, and so forth. Severe restrictions on the possibilities for quantitative analysis are obviously entailed by these limitations, which is why we stated that rankings constitute a relatively poor kind of measurement.

SCALES OF MEASUREMENT

The theory of measurement deals with the use of numbers to represent certain characteristic properties of systems and their components. It might seem as if the only problem of such a theory would be how to obtain the numbers—in short, how to take the measure. This is not the case. Perhaps it is surprising that the major problem dealt with in the theory of measurement is what can be done with the numbers once they have been obtained. There are two main reasons for being somewhat surprised about this. First, it is hard to resist thinking that numbers are, after all, just numbers. While numbers may represent the characteristics of systems, in the last analysis it is still true that they

---

[5] Or any of the infinity of other possibilities.

are not the characteristics—but numbers. Hence, one should do whatever one does with any other numbers. For the second, let us turn to what Humpty Dumpty said about the meanings of words, *viz.*: "It's just a question of who is going to be master!" (i.e., the words or their meanings). In other words, is the master of numbers the characteristics or do numbers make the characteristics subservient? The answer is more complex than one would immediately suspect. The obvious reply is that one rules the numbers and this approach has been consistently practiced, if not preached, by analysts in many different areas. Despite this fact, it is an out-and-out blunder to reason in this way.

The two arguments have a common refutation. Alice should have answered Humpty Dumpty: "You can be the master of meaning of your words if you want but no one will necessarily understand you. Assuming that you want to communicate you have to presume that the words you use have the meanings given in the dictionary." Probably Lewis Carroll would have given Humpty Dumpty an answer to squelch such an argument. But we are drawing an analogy between the meanings of words and the meanings of numbers. Our reply to both arguments is that only those arithmetical manipulations are permissible which correspond to a meaningful manipulation of the object being measured. With numbers, we can do *as we please* but with measurements we can only do what reality *permits* us to do.

The usual conception of what is permissible comes from our familiarity with a specific kind of measurement. An example is the measurement of weight. We manipulate numbers which represent weights with complete freedom. For instance, in discussing the weights of a 5-pound sack of sugar and a 10-pound sack of sugar we feel perfectly comfortable in saying that the total weight would be 15 pounds (by addition), that the second sack is 5 pounds heavier than the first (by subtraction), that the second sack is twice as heavy as the first (by multiplication), or that the first sack is half the weight of the second (by division). This granted, it is only natural to assume that we have similar flexibility with other kinds of measurement problems—but this is not the case.

The technical term for the type of measurement scale which permits the kind of flexibility illustrated above is *ratio scale*. Weight is measured on a ratio scale; consequently, all the usual arithmetical operations are permissible. In contradistinction, there are common enough kinds of measurement, e.g. temperature, which demonstrate that not all measurement scales are of the ratio type. Consider two rooms with temperatures that are respectively 40 and 80 degrees Fahrenheit. It seems reasonable (in the sense that it "feels right") to refer to an average temperature of $(40 + 80)/2 = 60$ degrees Fahrenheit. It seems quite wrong to say that one room is twice as hot as the other. It is hard to decide what it means to say that one room is 40 degrees Fahrenheit hotter than the other. The distinctions drawn by these statements are learned (in the sense that the meaning of language is learned). The reason for them is ordinarily unconscious. The technical term for the type of measurement scale exemplified by temperature is an *interval scale*. Only by understanding the distinctions between ratio and interval scales can one hope to understand the manipulations of numbers that are allowable under varying circumstances.

Let us develop the relevant differences between these scales in terms of phenomena with which everyone is familiar. Weight, for example, can be measured equally well in units of pounds or of kilograms. We know that there should be no difference between the conclusions that would be reached about an object simply because of our choice of units. This means that in establishing a ratio scale (typified by weight) the measurer has one choice which he can freely make, i.e., the unit of measurement. Once this selection has been made—be it in pound, kilogram, or stone—the whole scale is determined. Algebraically, if X is the weight in some specific unit, then $Y = bX$ would be the weight on another scale—where b units of the second kind make one unit of the first kind.

On the other hand, consider the two best known ways of measuring temperature: Fahrenheit and Centigrade scales. The well-known procedure for converting from Fahrenheit temperatures to the corresponding Centigrade measurements is to use the equation: $C = -\dfrac{160}{9} + \dfrac{5}{9}F$, where F and C are the number of degrees on their respective scales. To some, this equation may seem more familiar in verbal form, *viz.*, subtract 32 from the Fahrenheit temperature, then take 5⁄9 of the result to get the Centigrade temperature. The important point to notice is that there is more than one number involved. We need only one number to convert centimeters to inches, multiplying by 2.54; only one number is required to convert pounds to kilograms, multiplying by 2.2. Instead, two numbers are needed: *first*, subtract 32, *second*, multiply by 5⁄9. Algebraically, this is expressed as follows: if X is the measurement on one interval scale then $Y = a + cX$ will be the measurement on another interval scale, which is identified by specific values of a and c.

The difference between ratio and interval scales also can be explained verbally. There is one "free" choice for a ratio scale; two "free" choices for an interval scale. The one "free" choice for the ratio scale corresponds to the "b" in $Y = bX$; the two "free" choices in the interval scale correspond to the "a" and the "c" in $Y = a + cX$. Further, a ratio scale has a *natural zero*, which is why the measurer has only one choice available, i.e., the unit of measurement. Since an interval scale does not have a natural zero, the measurer must select his zero point as well as the unit of measurement. And what is a "natural zero"? A natural zero exists if there is a satisfactory answer to the question: Is there a real meaning to have nothing or none of the quantity being measured? The notion of having no, or zero, weight has a straightforward meaning. Neither Fahrenheit nor Centigrade embody a natural interpretation of "no temperature." [6] What are the implications of these differences between ratio and interval scales? Especially, what can be said about the allowable arithmetical manipulations on numbers that represent measurements for each type of scale? The answer to these questions follows directly from a basic principle. The principle is that only those operations can be permitted such that no *real world characteristic* will change as a consequence of our selection of the units of measurement. In algebraic terms this can be formulated as follows. Suppose we have two measurements, X_1 and X_2, and that we perform an arithmetical operation on them which yields a resulting number V. Now assume that with a different choice of units the two measurements would have been Y_1 and Y_2. We perform the same arithmetical manipulations on Y_1 and Y_2 as we did on the X's with the result W. Then we require either that W should bear the same relationship to V as the Y's bear to the X's or that $W = V$. The latter would be the case, for example, if we take the ratio of a circle's circumference to its diameter—no matter in what units the radius is measured. If these results were to depend on the units chosen, this would violate the principle we stated above.

Ratio scale

In this case we have already seen that the relationship which must exist between the Y's and the X's would be: $Y_1 = bX_1$ and $Y_2 = bX_2$. We therefore require that $W = bV$ or $W = V$ for any permissible arithmetical manipulation. Let us try a few cases.

---

[6] The Kelvin scale of temperature has a natural zero. It is $-273.16°C$, called absolute zero. This follows from work in physics where both theory and experiment indicate that a limit exists to the lowest possible temperature that can be achieved, i.e., absolute zero.

1. Average.
   This operation is allowable since it is given that $(X_1 + X_2)/2 = V$, then

   $$\frac{Y_1 + Y_2}{2} = \frac{bX_1 + bX_2}{2} = bV.$$

   It is also given that $(Y_1 + Y_2)/2 = W$; consequently $W = bV$, as required.
2. Difference.
   This operation is allowable since it is given that $X_1 - X_2 = V$, then

   $$Y_1 - Y_2 = bX_1 - bX_2 = bV.$$

   It is also given that $Y_1 - Y_2 = W$; consequently $W = bV$, as required.
3. Division.
   This operation is allowable since it is given that $X_1/X_2 = V$; then

   $$\frac{Y_1}{Y_2} = \frac{bX_1}{bX_2} = V.$$

   It is also given that $Y_1/Y_2 = W$; consequently $W = V$, as required.

Interval scale

For this scale we know that the relationship between the X's and the Y's would be: $Y_1 = a + cX_1$ and $Y_2 = a + cX_2$. We require either that $W = a + cV$ or that $W = V$ for any arithmetic manipulation to be permissible. Taking the same examples as we did for the ratio scale:

1. Average.
   This operation is allowable since it is given that $(X_1 + X_2)/2 = V$, then

   $$\frac{Y_1 + Y_2}{2} = \frac{a + cX_1 + a + cX_2}{2} = \frac{2a + c(X_1 + X_2)}{2} = a + cV.$$

   It is also given that $(Y_1 + Y_2)/2 = W$; consequently $W = a + cV$, as required.

2. Difference.

This operation is *not* allowable since it is given that $X_1 - X_2 = V$, then

$$Y_1 - Y_2 = (a + cX_1) - (a + cX_2) = c(X_1 - X_2).$$

It is also given that $Y_1 - Y_2 = W$; consequently $W = cV$, not $W = a + cV$ as required.

3. Division.

This operation *not* allowable since it is given that $X_1/X_2 = V$, then

$$\frac{Y_1}{Y_2} = \frac{a + cX_1}{a + cX_2}.$$

It is also given that $Y_1/Y_2 = W$; clearly

$$W \neq a + cV.$$

We see that our natural inclination concerning the way we talk about temperature is justified. Also, we have tried to clarify why it is that our intuition cannot resolve questions involving operations which are "impossible" for certain types of scales.

The relation of this discussion to the problem of measuring utility should be apparent. Assuming that we can measure utility, what kind of measurement might be involved? The three major theoretical alternatives are: (1) ordinal measurement (i.e., rankings), (2) interval measurement, and (3) ratio measurement. There has been much discussion of these questions in the literature, and it is evident that the question is a vexed one.[7] A fair summary of the positions might be as follows:

> If multiple objectives exist, then it is probable that not even ordinal measurement can be accomplished. The difficulties in this kind of situation were previously referred to as the problem of dimensionality. With only one objective there *is* general agreement that ordinal measurement can be accomplished. At the same time, there is a sizable group of authorities who maintain that more than ordinal measure, namely interval measure, can be achieved. No one maintains that utility can be measured on a ratio scale, even though there is nothing conclusive to show that it cannot be done.

[7] A good treatment will be found in Tapas Majumdar, *The Measurement of Utility* (New York: St. Martin's Press, Inc., 1958).

A first step, if we hope to move further than rankings, might reasonably consist of some procedure for measuring utility on an interval scale. (This is the subject of our next section.) To shift from an ordinal to an interval scale represents no trivial improvement. As an example of the implications of such a change, with ranked data as our measure of utility, we cannot calculate expected values. But if utility can be measured on an interval scale, we can base our analyses on expected values (as previously shown). Since the use of expected values is of major importance in decision theory, it would be most desirable to achieve an interval scale measurement of utility whenever possible.

THE STANDARD GAMBLE

That it is often possible to achieve an interval scale for the measurement of utility was demonstrated by John von Neumann and Oskar Morgenstern.[8] The procedure they developed for doing this is known as the standard-gamble method. It is an extremely ingenious way to determine an individual utility scale for outcomes, and we will present the essentials of this technique in the next several paragraphs.

The idea of the standard gamble is to give the decision-maker pairs of alternatives between which he must choose. Let us return to the administrator who was faced with the decision problem in labor rela-

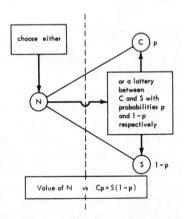

FIGURE 4.1 The standard gamble can be used to obtain interval scale measures of utility.

[8] John von Neumann and Oskar Morgenstern, *Theory of Games and Economic Behavior* (Princeton, N. J.: Princeton University Press, 1947), pp. 15-30.

tions. His three alternatives, it will be remembered, were ranked in order (1) C (for contract), (2) N (for negotiations), and (3) S (for strike). We have shown now why it is that almost no arithmetical manipulations are permissible on the numbers assigned as ranks for these three outcomes. It would help us greatly if we could instead determine three numbers that would measure the administrator's utilities for the three possible outcomes on an interval scale. This is what the standard-gamble approach attempts to accomplish.

Suppose we ask this administrator to express his preference between: Choice 1, getting N certainly; and Choice 2, a lottery in which he will get C with probability p, and S with probability $1 - p$. The reader should meditate for a moment on exactly what we are asking the administrator to tell us—his preference between having N for sure and taking a gamble on C or S. We propose to adjust p. Thus, suppose we set $p = 1$. This would mean that the administrator was being asked to choose between N for sure and C for sure—and we already know he will select C. Suppose we put $p = 0$. This would mean that we are asking him to choose between N for sure and S for sure—and we know already that he would select N. But this would indicate that as p changes from 0 to 1, the administrator's preference for N (Alternative 1) instead of the lottery (Alternative 2) must switch at some point to a preference for the lottery over N. It seems reasonable, then, to say that the preferences are equal at that value of p for which this switch occurs. For example, the manager might say that he has equal preferences when $p = .9$.

We know from prior discussion that for an interval scale there are two "free" choices. In the standard-gamble procedure we are instructed to exercise these choices in a particular way. We always assign 0 to the worst outcome and 1 to the best. From our ranked ordering it follows that we must set $S = 0$ and $C = 1$. In accordance with the underlying theory we now require that all other measurements (in this example there is only one other) should be measurable on the interval scale that we have now established. Von Neumann and Morgenstern proved that the measurement for N is the value of p at which there was indifference and thereby equal utility for N and for the lottery (in the above case $N = .9$).

If there were more outcomes we would repeat the same procedure for each outcome. The indifference value of p would be the interval measure for the given outcome. So it is an easy matter to extend this procedure to any desired number of outcomes. For each outcome with an intermediate rank we find the probability at which no preference exists between certainty of that outcome and the given lottery between the two extreme outcomes. The probability determined in this way is the measure of utility for that outcome. Naturally, there are limitations to the validity of this procedure. The most important one which we should note is that transitivity should hold between preferences for outcomes. This means, as we have seen, that the outcomes can be ranked—which is equivalent to saying that only a single dimension is involved.

The advantage of this particular measurement technique results directly from the fact that von Neumann and Morgenstern proved that it yielded an interval scale. This means that the administrator can now utilize analytical procedures requiring the calculation of expected values. He does this knowing that he will be entirely consistent in his actions. There are other advantages as well. The standard-gamble approach permits information about managerial values to be transmitted in an operational form to subordinates. And in general, the standard gamble fosters the construction of more suitable, theoretical frameworks for the decision process. For a more detailed account of the procedure, including various other restrictions, the interested reader should see Chapter 2 of Luce and Raiffa's *Games and Decisions*.[9]

It should be noted that attempts to use this technique in actual practice have not always been successful. Sometimes there are inconsistencies in the stated preferences and no unique measure of utility can be constructed. But, as L. J. Savage has pointed out,[10] often this means no more than that the individual in question is really inconsistent and, when it is pointed out to him, he will attempt to eliminate the inconsistency. Certainly it is not always the case that inconsistencies can be blamed on multidimensionality.

Another difficulty arises if one of the outcomes is overwhelmingly bad—say bankruptcy. The possible effect of this on the standard-gamble approach can be understood by the reader if he will envision himself using the method to evaluate his utilities for the following three outcomes: make $1000, lose $50, die. Perhaps it is the case that no rational person should prefer any lottery involving death as one of the alternatives to losing $50. One possible answer to this quandary is to note that even an entirely rational person might prefer the lottery between death and making $1000 to the certainty of losing $50 if the

[9] R. Duncan Luce and Howard Raiffa, *Games and Decisions* (New York: John Wiley & Sons, Inc., 1958).
[10] L. J. Savage, *The Foundations of Statistics* (New York: John Wiley & Sons, Inc., 1954).

probability of death were so small as to make it virtually impossible —say 1 divided by the number of fundamental particles in the universe. But one difficulty with this answer is that people seem to be unable to distinguish realistically between small differences in probabilities that might make large differences in utilities. It is probably more realistic to accept the fact that a special case arises when one or more of the outcomes are overwhelmingly bad. We noted this same kind of difficulty when discussing the logarithmic representation of utility.

We see that we are not completely helpless when faced with non-quantitative objectives in a decision problem. On the contrary, there are several possible ways in which we can proceed to obtain a quantitative payoff. None of them is perfectly satisfactory. Each is subject to limitations but, nonetheless, for many typical organizational objectives that are not obviously quantifiable, a payoff can be obtained.

Finally, the standard-gamble method sometimes can be used for those cases where several different objectives are involved simultaneously. The problem in such cases is to obtain a payoff measure that incorporates the utilities of all of the objectives—each achieved to a different degree. If the rankings are confused by multidimensionality there may not be much that can be done to clarify the situation. Often, however, the manager can approximate the utilities of the various outcomes by using the standard-gamble approach.

STRATEGIES AND STATES OF NATURE

So far we have considered the need and difficulty of formulating the objectives of the decision-maker as precisely as possible. We have also discussed the problems and possibilities of determining a quantitative measure of payoff. But our preliminary survey of the decision problem revealed the need for two additional components: strategies and states of nature. We must now consider these in more detail.

We have previously explained that strategies are based upon the resources under the manager's control. As a decision-maker, he has alternative ways in which he can use his resources. The strategy which he selects is his decision as to what he will *do* with the resources under his control. The use of the word "resources" is justifiable since some kind of disposition of resources is usually involved in all potential organizational strategies. The manager's own time and effort can be included. But it may be misleading because some decisions use up only the manager's time and effort—and no resources, in the strict sense of the word, are affected. For example, the decision problem of pricing a new product does not require allocation of resources. Neither, for that matter, does the decision to *wait and see* involve the disposition of resources. Nevertheless, in its broadest sense, all of the talents, abilities, and experiences of the managerial staff are resources of the organization. There is no particular need to emphasize this fact since most decision problems involve the allocation of physical resources and the decision-maker's strategy is the plan for their allocation.

At first thought it might appear that there are virtually an unlimited number of possible strategies in any realistic decision problem. In fact, there are often a great many, but various factors serve to limit the number of strategies that will be considered as genuine possibilities in a given decision problem. To begin with, strategies will be considered unacceptable if they violate any laws. In frontier days, one of the better strategies in some competitive decision problems was to shoot your opponent. Today, the laws of the land prohibit such sharp competitive practices and we can only hope that they will be taken even more seriously. A whole range of strategies is prohibited by laws relevant to collusion between competitors. Another range of possible strategies is prohibited by the Pure Food and Drug Act. We could go on listing restrictions to strategies that arise from legal agencies, statutes, and the common law.

Even if there were no restrictions against bad practices, any organization with an eye on its public-relations objectives would hesitate to indulge in them. This indicates that a more fundamental restriction on strategies exists in the form of social mores and public opinion. The law, of course, is a reflection of these. Most organizations attempt to limit their strategies to those which are consonant with the socially accepted practices of their time and place. Such self-imposed restrictions go under the name of *policy*.

Policy is applied to situations not covered by the law, except for the primary policy: not to violate the law. In Chapter 3, we discussed policy in terms of conflict of objectives. At that time, we stated that policy was a collection of principles and rules whose purpose was to guide the manager and to help him consider things which he might otherwise overlook. We can now extend this thinking to the present context. Policy relieves the manager from having to consider a great many possibilities. It saves his time for decision elements that must be explored. If policy were stated in details instead of principles, it would not be an effective means of ruling out vast areas of possible strategies. To illustrate, it would be virtually impossible to play a good game of chess if every conceivable arrangement of pieces on the board had to be interpreted as a unique situation. For each situation there are so many possible strategies that a player who is not guided by policy must either play by memory or by chance. It is chess policy—the existence of principles stated in terms of general configurations—that permits the player to discard a great number of undesirable strategies. He discards them as classes of strategies, not one by one. In this same manner, the manager rejects whole classes of strategies.

Strategies that can be eliminated in lots rather than in units are *generalized strategies*. There are a number of methods for generalizing strategies so that they can be accepted or rejected in classes. Law, social mores, and policy provide this kind of discrimination. Usually, strategies eliminated by principles are those which would result in serious conflicts between the objectives of the organization and the vital objectives of society. The type of conflict is such that the organization does not care to be placed in the situation where it must choose between its own objectives and those of society. Since the position of having to make a choice is a compromising one—even if the decision is always in favor of society—the principles are ingrained in the decision-maker. He does not even consciously reject the strategies that lead to these conflicts. He never even considers them.

There are other situations in which the manager may eliminate a great number of possibilities, some of which are optimum solutions that in no way conflict with social, legal, or policy goals. The additional restrictions on strategic possibilities appear in two forms: (1) unthinking acceptance of the conventions and customs of an industry, and (2) an individual's reluctance to consider certain kinds of changes. In these cases, the *status quo* is taken for granted, but not with consistently desirable results. Yet there is hardly any awareness that another way might exist.

The fact that many strategies are never contemplated because of psychological deterrents is not an advantage. For example, a dress manufacturer who has been identified for years with the $14.95 line of dresses may have so profound a revulsion to the perfectly reasonable strategy of shifting to the $9.95 line that he is unable to conceive of this possibility. Similarly, the management of an organization that has been located for its entire existence in one particular area may have great antipathy to the sound strategy of moving to a new location that has lower labor costs, lower transportation costs, or some other vital advantage. Psychological deterrents to the recognition of possible strategies cut down the size of the decision problem, but many times the saving is obtained at the expense of a simultaneous cut in the degree of achievement of the objective.

Many trade customs are beneficial. Others, which serve as restrictions on the number of possible strategies, are neither beneficial nor harmful with respect to attaining objectives. Their consideration would add no advantage and subtract greatly from the manager's time. Therefore, in a sense, the inclusion of unusual or unthought-of strategies with high payoffs is reserved for a creative act on the part of the decision-maker. There is no way in which operations research, decision theory, or mathematics can replace such creative acts. In some fortunate cases, the result of the analytic approach brings certain elements or relationships to the attention of the decision-maker, and he is led to break through his barriers of bounded rationality. In fact, by introducing an external process of reasoning, analytical methods frequently act as a catalyst for creative thinking. This is strictly an empirical observation.

States of nature have many characteristics in common with strategies. Here, too, we want to be able to recognize as many states of nature as we possibly can. But faced with overwhelming numbers of states of nature, we want to know how to classify them so that we do not have to consider each detail in every possible form. The discovery of states of nature is not limited by law, social mores, or policy. Neither is it affected by custom. Psychological deterrents, on the other hand, do play a part. As in the case of strategies, the discovery of the relevant states of nature requires systematic exploration, the full utilization of experience, and, if we are lucky, some creative insights which escape the confines of our bounded rationality.

Competitive strategies are a special class of states of nature. It may seem that we should not be able to conceive of more strategic possibilities for our competitor than we can for ourselves. However, this may not always be the case. Sometimes, the competitor is in a distinctly different position than we are with respect to assets, volume, market share, product lines, and so on. Many times, we lack sufficient information about the competitor and this seriously handicaps our efforts to predict his possible behaviors. One thing we believe is that his behavior will not be dictated by chance. The importance of this fact becomes obvious when we discuss game theory.

For the moment, it will be sufficient to say that sometimes it is possible to list all relevant states of nature and all relevant competitive strategies. At the other extreme, however, we cannot hope to consider all possible shifts in the economy, calamities in nature, technological breakthroughs, fads in society (i.e., all possible states of nature and competitive strategies).

PROBLEMS

1. Practice in calculating expected values helps to make the concept a familiar one. Here is an assortment of expected value problems:

   a. A particular stock has paid dividends of $0.50 per share in 12 of the last 15 payments. The other three times it has paid $0.25. What is the expected dividend?

   b. A company that sells two different models of one item finds that 65 per cent of its customers buy the cheaper model, for $95. The remaining 35 per cent of its customers pay $125 for the more expensive model. What is the expected purchase price?

   c. A magazine discovers that 40 per cent of the families that subscribe are ones in which there are two wage earners. In the remaining 60 per cent of the families there is only one wage earner. What is the expected number of wage earners per subscribing family?

   d. A salesman makes 35 calls without a sale, and 15 calls with an average sale of $60. What is his expected sales per call?

   e. The same salesman has a particular trip of 48 miles which he often makes. Four times it takes him one hour and six times it takes him one and a half hours. What is the expected time for the trip? (Convert the data to miles per hour and calculate his expected speed. Compare the two answers. One must be careful in calculating expected values of rates!)

   f. A small-loan company finds that 12 per cent of its borrowers default on an average 20 per cent of their loans. What is the expected percentage default?

   g. A mail-order company finds that 18 per cent of the purchases of a particular item are returned. The company estimates that each return costs $0.70 in transportation and extra handling. What is the expected extra cost due to returns per unit of this item?

   h. A second-hand car lot has a mark-up of $250 on 65 per cent of its cars and a mark-up of $400 on the rest. What is the expected mark-up?

   i. A department store discovers that twice as many customers buy two units at $3.95 (for both) as buy one unit for $2.15. What is the expected purchase price per unit?

   j. A magazine states that the average number of cars per subscriber family is 1.2. If 20 per cent of the family subscribers have no car, what is the average number of cars per family of the families which do have one or more cars?

2. Suppose you have total capital of $5000. You have the opportunity to make a speculative investment of $2500 which will be either totally lost or worth $7500 in six months.

   a. Using expected values directly, what is the maximum probability of total loss for which this would be a profitable investment?
   b. Using the logarithmic measure of utility, what is the maximum probability of total loss for which this would be a profitable investment?
   c. Use the standard-gamble method to determine your own utilities for the three outcomes: $2500, $5000, $10,000. What is the maximum probability of a total loss that would be acceptable?
   d. Another mathematical form which can be used to represent utility is:

$$\text{Utility of } x \text{ dollars} = \log \frac{1 + \dfrac{x}{c}}{1 - \dfrac{x}{c}}$$

   where c is some constant larger than any of the x's involved. Try this form with several values of c and determine the maximum probability of a total loss which would be acceptable. How does this probability change with c?

3. A company with assets of $50,000 is considering the possibility of redesigning its product. Including new tools and dies, the total cost of the redesign job will be $12,000. The company estimates the profitability of the product for three alternatives, No Change, Design 1, and Design 2. The new designs, 1 and 2, have the same cost.

NO CHANGE		DESIGN 1		DESIGN 2	
PROFIT (PER YEAR)	PROBABILITY	PROFIT (PER YEAR)	PROBABILITY	PROFIT (PER YEAR)	PROBABILITY
$4000	0.2	$8000	0.2	$6000	0.4
5000	0.5	9000	0.5	9000	0.2
6000	0.3	10000	0.3	12000	0.4

   a. Compare the dollar expected values of total assets at the end of one year for each alternative strategy.
   b. Compare the dollar expected values of total assets at the end of two years for each alternative strategy.
   c. How long a period is required before the total assets obtained from Design 1 are equal to the assets if no change is made? How long for Design 2?
   d. Instead of dollar expected values use the logarithmic measure of utility to answer questions a. and b. Comment on the differences resulting from the use of each method.

4. *A* reports to *B*, *B* reports to *C*, *C* reports to *D*, *D* reports to *A*, *A* reports to *C*, and *D* reports to *B*. Which relationships are transitive and which are not?

5. Determine the expected value of the executive's bonus if, for the past 15 years, he has received $200 five times and $300 ten times and the system can be considered stable. If the executive has $10,000 in the bank, what per cent increase does each possible bonus make? Using the log utility assumption, what per cent increase in utility will each possible bonus contribute? What can we say about these results?

6. Rank-order your preferences for the following business conditions (*H* = high, *L* = low):

PRICE	SALES VOLUME	COST OF MANUFACTURING	COST OF SELLING
L	L	H	H
H	H	L	H
L	L	L	H
H	H	H	L
H	L	H	L
L	L	H	L
L	H	L	L

How many possible rankings are there? Does it seem possible that a manager could consider all of these? What happens if we describe the condition of each of the variables with high, low, and medium? What happens if we describe each variable with any number between 0 and 100? Check each column after ranking for transitivity. What does this tell us about the manager's decision problem? What consequences are there if a manager is not transitive in his decision-making?

7. Use the standard gamble on the outcomes you have ranked in problem 6, above. First obtain *p* values for ranking numbers 1-2-7, 1-3-7, 1-4-7, 1-5-7, and 1-6-7. Then repeat the procedure for 1-2-3, 1-3-5, 1-4-6, and 3-5-7. Check your results against the first five *p* values which you derived.

8. For the self-insurance problem discussed in this chapter, the insurance company asked a $1500 premium to insure a $10,000 shipment with a 0.10 probability of loss. The company had assets of $100,000. How much could it afford to pay the shipper above $10,000 so that it would have no gain in utility?

9. Here is an example of behavior which would be irrational if dollars always measured the utility of dollars. A lottery might involve the sale of 100,000 tickets at $.50 each, with the prize being a car worth $6,000. Many supposedly rational persons buy a ticket in such a lottery.

    a. Analyze this speculation in terms of the expected dollar values of the two courses of action.

    b. What relationship does this example suggest about utility scales and dollar amounts? Is this in agreement with the conclusions based on self-insurance?

10. The "numbers game" is a widely played, but illegal, gambling procedure. A given amount is bet on a three-digit number, e.g., 583. A three-digit number is drawn randomly. If it is 583 the bettor is paid 600 times the amount that he bet. Since the numbers game is commonly played by poor people in large metropolitan areas, it is a convenient political whipping boy. Do such attacks make sense?

    a. Analyze this problem in terms of the expected values of dollars, assuming a $.10 bet.

    b. Contrast the numbers game with sources of small loans likely to be available to the bettors. As an example, "loan sharks" who often exact 20 per cent interest per week.

    c. Contrast the numbers game with alternative ways to buy a television set on the installment plan.

    d. Similarly contrast the numbers game with prepaid medical plans.

5 | The Analysis of Decisions

THE PAYOFF MATRIX

Mathematics suggests a convenient way to present our breakdown of the decision problem. This is to put it in the form of a matrix—called the *payoff matrix*. A matrix is simply a two-dimensional array of figures arranged in rows and columns. A matrix representation of the decision problem is particularly convenient because we can let the rows be the available strategies (one row for each strategy) and the columns be the states of nature (one column for each state of nature). When appropriate, the columns can reflect competitive actions just as well.

The entry at the intersection of each row and column is the payoff —the measure of the utility of that specific outcome which occurs for a given strategy and a particular state of nature. Thus, the payoff matrix summarizes all of the characteristics of the decision problem which we have been discussing. Symbolically, the payoff matrix looks like Table 5.1—using N's to designate states of nature, S's to designate strategies, and P's to designate payoffs. The decision problem is the same as always—to select a specific strategy. The payoff matrix provides a means of structuring and presenting the relevant information.

The payoff matrix representation of a decision problem seems so apt for its purpose that it is easy to overlook the question of whether it can always be accomplished. Can every decision problem be put into

TABLE 5.1

	N_1	N_2	N_3	N_4	. . .	N_j
S_1:	P_{11}	P_{12}	P_{13}	P_{14}	. . .	. . .
S_2:	P_{21}	P_{22}	P_{23}	P_{24}	. . .	. . .
. . .	. . .	. . .	. . .	. . .	. . .	
S_i:	. . .	. . .	. . .	. . .	. . .	P_{ij}

a payoff matrix format? The answer is that the great majority of decision problems can be represented in payoff matrix form. However, in many instances how to do it is not obvious. Difficulties arise as soon as it is necessary to consider a sequence of decisions as if they were one overall decision. For example, consider the problem of sampling the quality of a production run to determine whether to accept the entire "lot." There is a preliminary decision to take a particular size sample. Then after determining how many defectives there are in the sample, a subsequent decision must be made to accept or to reject the lot. This is a typical problem involving a sequence of decisions. There are really two separate decisions. There are also two sets of states of nature. First, there is the unknown percentage of defectives that are actually in the lot. Second, there are different possible numbers of defectives which may be found in the sample—granting any specific number of defectives in the lot. How can a problem such as this be put in payoff matrix form? As another example, remember that the columns of the payoff matrix can represent competitive actions. Consequently, any game with a sequence of moves creates similar difficulties.

Let us put the problem under consideration into perspective. It is our purpose to analyze decision problems in such a way that we can recommend to the manager a particular strategy which he should select for a specific case. It turns out that the payoff matrix provides a remarkably good structure for this analysis. We must also know how universal the payoff matrix representation is, since we would like our analytical efforts to be as generally applicable as possible. It must be emphasized, however, that the payoff matrix is simply a methodological convenience which in no way precludes the possibility that other bases for analyses can be found. Alternatives become especially important if the payoff matrix for a particular decision problem cannot be determined.

Returning to the example of acceptance sampling, a difficulty occurs because the payoff matrix format requires the selection of *one* strategy, given that *one* state of nature holds, not several. Fortunately, the difficulty can be overcome by a suitable statement of what we mean by a strategy. Then, the lot acceptance example becomes quite straightforward. A strategy statement for the overall decision problem becomes something like this. Take a sample of size 10. Reject the lot if there is any defective product in the sample; otherwise accept it. Redefinitions of the states of nature are required also. The effect of this transformation of terms is to drastically increase the number of strategies that must be considered. For our immediate purposes, this is only a technical problem. Indeed, the payoff matrix for this problem can be constructed. Through this example we have tried to emphasize that the payoff matrix representation can frequently be achieved—even in cases where, at first glance, it might seem otherwise.

SEVERAL KINDS OF DECISIONS

There are many ways to classify decision problems. But for our purposes there is one kind of classification which is crucial. This is a classification based on the amount of information available to the decision-maker about the likelihood of occurrence of the various states of nature. Five main classes of decision problems exist in accord with this classification. Important procedural differences are associated with these decision problem classes. Therefore, we must clearly distinguish between them.

Decision-making under certainty occurs when we have a decision problem in which we know with certainty which state of nature will occur. This means, in other words, that there is only one column in our payoff matrix. Alternatively, this kind of decision problem considers only one relevant payoff for each possible strategy. At first, this may seem like a trivial case. How can there be any difficulty in reaching the best decision if there is only one column? Simply read down the column to find the largest payoff and that will be the optimum strategy. But it isn't quite that simple. The idea behind the suggestion is absolutely correct, but the difficulty is that there may be such an enormous number of strategy rows that it would be quite impossible to list them.

Of what use then, is a payoff matrix which can't even be written down? The answer is that in some cases, when the actual payoff matrix can't be constructed, it still remains an effective means of conceptualizing the problem. As we shall see, one of the contributions of operations research to decision-making is in this realm. For the present, it suffices to indicate that real and important decision problems of this type exist.

Suppose, for example, that you run a machine shop and have 20 contracts for machined parts. You also have 20 machines, any one of which could do any one of the contracts. But since the machines are of different designs, intended for different purposes, each type would require differing amounts of time for each contract—and, hence, would be more or less expensive. Quite naturally, you would like to assign the jobs to the machines so as to minimize the total cost. The first job could be assigned to any one of the 20 machines, the second job to any one of the remaining 19, the third job to any one of the remaining 18, and so forth. So the total number of ways in which you could assign the jobs is given by $20 \times 19 \times 18 \times 17 \times 16 \times 15 \ldots \times 3 \times 2 \times 1$, and if one takes the trouble to do the arithmetic he will find that the total number of ways to assign the jobs to the machines is 2.4329×10^{18} where we have rounded off the number. Now, each way of assigning these jobs to machines is another possible strategy, so this decision problem's payoff matrix would have only one column (because the costs of the various machines are assumed known), but it would have almost $2\frac{1}{2}$ quintillion rows. That such a modest problem could produce so many rows in the payoff matrix may be surprising. It does serve to show that decision-making under certainty can be a genuine problem. And this sort of problem is by no means confined to machine shops. On the contrary, a great number of different kinds of organizational decision problems fall into the category of decision-making under certainty.

The second kind of decision problem occurs where there are a number of states of nature but where the decision-maker *knows* the probability of occurrence of each of the states of nature. This kind of situation is called *decision-making under risk*. For the purpose of illustration, consider the decision problem facing a gambler—where the possible states of nature are the various chance events, the probabilities of which can be calculated by probability theory. Typically in many organizational problems, the probabilities of the various states of nature are known by virtue of determining how frequently they occurred in the past. Thus, the decision problem of a manufacturer of antifreeze could involve various weather conditions. The probabilities of occurrence of these different states of nature might be determined from past experience. Similarly, inventory decision problems involving parts for factory or office equipment would include those states of nature that represent the various rates of failure of the parts, and these probabilities might be known from past experience. This kind of decision problem occurs frequently.

The third kind of decision problem is *decision-making under uncer-*

tainty, where the probabilities of occurrence of the various states of
nature are not known, or where, if one is an objectivist, the very idea
of probability descriptions for the states of nature is meaningless. Such
problems arise wherever there is no basis in past experience for estimating the probabilities of occurrence of the relevant states of nature.
The decision problems involved in marketing a new product would
include various levels of demand as states of nature. Yet there is no
past experience on which to base estimates of the relevant probabilities
as there is in the case of established products. Decision problems concerning expansion of facilities may have states of nature including such
things as war, depression, recession, and inflation. How can probabilities be estimated for these states of nature? Many decision problems of
major importance are of this kind.

The huge gap in the availability of information between the second
and the third categories suggests the need for a fourth category: *decision-making under partial information.* In reaching decisions under
risk, we assume that the decision-maker knows the probability of occurrence of each state of nature. Consider an inventory problem. The
states of nature are demand levels; the strategies are the quantities to
order. For this to be a decision problem under risk it is necessary that
the demand distribution be completely known. For the same problem
under uncertainty we assume that nothing whatsoever is known about
the demand distribution. What, then, about the intermediate cases,
where *something,* but *not everything,* is known about the demand distribution? For example, some of the standard measures of descriptive
statistics (such as averages, medians, or modes) might be known without knowing the whole demand distribution, e.g., the exact form of the
distribution, such as normal, binomial, or Poisson. Thus, we could
know that average demand was 100 units and that the standard devia-
tion was 10 units—but nothing else. It is such cases as these that are
included in the category of decision problems under partial information. It may be the most common category of "real" decision problems.
However, since somewhat more sophisticated procedures are required
in dealing with this kind of decision problem many decision-makers
act as though the problem was one of risk with varying degrees of pen-
alty. Although we shall not discuss these kinds of problems in this
book, it was essential for classification purposes to mention them.[1]

The last category of decision problems that we require is *decision-
making under conflict.* Here the columns of the payoff matrix represent

[1] This kind of decision problem is discussed at some length in Martin K. Starr
and David W. Miller, *Inventory Control, Theory and Practice* (Englewood Cliffs,
N.J.: Prentice-Hall, Inc., 1962).

strategies of rational opponents rather than states of nature. The essence of this kind of decision problem is that the decision-maker is involved in some kind of competitive situation with a rational opponent. Military weapon and logistic systems and marketplace brand competition epitomize this class of decision-making—but even ordinary parlor games provide perfectly good illustrations. Decision-making under conflict is the subject studied in the theory of games. The title, "theory of games," may suggest frivolity. Nothing could be further from the truth. The essence of games (in the sense of the theory of games) is the presence of conflict of interest between two or more rational opponents. The grimness of war, the tensions of nuclear diplomacy, and the nature of business competition are all we need consider to deny the frivolity of the concept of games. There are many important and serious exemplifications of decision-making under conflict.

DECISION CRITERION UNDER CERTAINTY

Now that we have briefly outlined the various kinds of decision problems, we can turn to the basic question: How should a specific strategy be selected? In other words, how should the decision be made? What we want to investigate is the reasonable procedure or procedures by which a decision can be reached once we have developed the payoff matrix. We would like to find a *criterion* for each class of decision by which the decision-maker, given his payoff matrix, can select his strategy.

There is no difficulty, *in theory*, in determining the decision criterion under certainty. All we need do is find the strategy which has the largest payoff and that is the strategy which should be selected. There is no possible reason for doing otherwise. Each strategy has only one payoff, since there is a single column in the payoff matrix when the state of nature is certainly known. Since the payoff represents the degree of achievement of the objective, the largest payoff is the best one that can be found for the chosen objective. The decision criterion, then, is: Select that strategy which has the largest payoff. The practical difficulty which arises when the number of strategies is enormous must be dealt with by such methods of operations research as linear programming.

DECISION CRITERION UNDER RISK

What happens in the case of decision-making under risk? Here we no longer have just one payoff for each strategy. Instead, there are a number of payoffs—one for each possible state of nature. So a decision criterion for risk will either have to be based on all of the possible payoffs for each strategy, or on one or more payoffs selected according to some rule.

Let us take a simple decision problem under risk as an example. Assume that a processor of frozen vegetables has to decide what crop to plant in a particular area. Suppose that the strategies are only two: to plant peas, or asparagus, and that the states of nature can be summarized in three possibilities: perfect weather, variable weather, and bad weather. On the basis of weather records it is determined that the probability of perfect weather is 0.25, the probability of variable weather is 0.50, and the probability of bad weather is 0.25. The dollar yields of the two crops under these different conditions are known and the decision-maker's utility is assumed to be measured by the dollar amounts. All of this information can be summarized in a payoff matrix:

	N_1	N_2	N_3
PROBABILITY:	0.25	0.50	0.25
	PERFECT WEATHER	VARIABLE WEATHER	BAD WEATHER
S_1: Plant peas	$40,000	$30,000	$20,000
S_2: Plant asparagus	$70,000	$20,000	$ 0

What strategy should the decision-maker select? The rational individual, under these circumstances, will govern his selection of strategies by the *expected utility* of the strategies. He will select that strategy which has the largest expected utility.

We introduced the notion of expected values earlier. Using P_{ij} to designate the payoff for the ith strategy and the jth state of nature and p_j to designate the probability of the jth state of nature, it follows that the expected value of the payoff for the ith strategy, S_i, is

$$\text{EV } (S_i) = P_{i1}p_1 + P_{i2}p_2 + P_{i3}p_3 + \ldots + P_{in}p_n$$

$$= \sum_{j=1}^{j=n} P_{ij}p_j$$

where EV (S_i) designates the expected payoff for the strategy denoted by S_i. (Remember that an expected value is the simple arithmetic mean or average.)

Using the equation above, we can calculate the expected payoff for each of the two strategies in our example.

$$EV\ (S_1) = \$40,000(\tfrac{1}{4}) + \$30,000(\tfrac{1}{2}) + \$20,000(\tfrac{1}{4}) = \$30,000$$
$$EV\ (S_2) = \$70,000(\tfrac{1}{4}) + \$20,000(\tfrac{1}{2}) + 0(\tfrac{1}{4}) = \$27,500$$

The expected payoff for Strategy 1 is larger; this is the strategy that should be selected. The food processor should choose the alternative: plant peas. Why? Because if the same decision situation were presented to him a great number of times he would average $2500 more from Strategy 1 than he would from Strategy 2.

But, one may think, aren't there other factors to consider besides the expected value? For example, let us suppose that the probabilities were different. Suppose the probabilities were $\tfrac{1}{2}$, $\tfrac{3}{8}$, and $\tfrac{1}{8}$, respectively, for the three states of nature. Then the expected payoffs for the two strategies would be:

$$EV\ (S_1) = \$40,000(\tfrac{1}{2}) + \$30,000(\tfrac{3}{8}) + \$20,000(\tfrac{1}{8}) = \$33,750$$
$$EV\ (S_2) = \$70,000(\tfrac{1}{2}) + \$20,000(\tfrac{3}{8}) + 0(\tfrac{1}{8}) = \$42,500$$

And, since the expected payoff for Strategy 2 is larger, this should be the choice of the food processor. At this point one might say: On the face of it, I disagree! Look at the difference between the payoffs. If the processor chooses to plant asparagus (S_2), the expected payoff is higher because of the much higher return on asparagus with perfect weather. But if he plants asparagus and has bad weather, he doesn't make anything at all. Whereas, if he plants peas he may not make as much when the weather is perfect, but he never risks having no return at all. So why wouldn't a perfectly rational person prefer to forego some expected payoff in order to avoid the possibility of no return at all? It might be said that he was paying the difference in expected payoffs as a premium on insurance against having no return.

This argument only appears to present a valid objection to the rule that the strategy with the highest expected payoff should be chosen. In fact, the objection is misplaced. A completely rational decision-maker might well reject Strategy 2 (plant asparagus), but it is because his utility for dollars is not properly measured by the dollar amounts. In short, for this case, the payoffs are wrong.

The same kind of problem was discussed in Chapter 4—the context being the self-insurance problem. It is an important point and deserves emphasis. Any argument against the criterion of choosing the best expected value (for a specific decision problem under risk) implies that the decision-maker has some other objective than just dollar amounts. Here it is the objective of having some control over his income. In the self-insurance problem it was the objective of avoiding the possibility of ruin. Criticism of the expected value criterion (for risk) is directed against the wrong part of the analysis. It is never a question of the criterion being wrong, but rather that the payoffs have been incorrectly measured to reflect the decision-maker's utilities for the outcomes.

If the food processor was able to utilize a procedure for measuring his utility, he should then be able to demonstrate the correctness of the expected value criterion. In our present example, suppose that the dollar amounts do not adequately represent the decision-maker's utility. Consequently, he turns to the standard-gamble procedure to measure his utilities for the various outcomes. There are five possible outcomes: $70,000, $40,000, $30,000, $20,000, and 0. To determine this manager's utilities for the intermediate amounts we would present him with the usual choices. First, would he prefer $40,000 certainly to a lottery between $70,000 with probability $4/7$ and 0 dollars with probability of $3/7$? In the case we are considering he would prefer the certainty of $40,000. So, we would adjust the probability upward until he indicated no preference. This *might* occur at a probability of $6/7$ of getting the $70,000. We would proceed similarly with the other two outcomes and *might* find the no-preference probability for $30,000 at $p = 9/14$ and the no-preference probability for $20,000 at $p = 3/7$. This would then give us the utilities for the five possible outcomes as follows:

OUTCOME	UTILITY
$70,000	1
$40,000	$6/7 = 0.857$
$30,000	$9/14 = 0.643$
$20,000	$3/7 = 0.429$
0	0

Our payoff matrix would then be:

0.857	0.643	0.429
1.000	0.429	0.000

We now proceed to calculate the expected payoffs as before (using, in this case, the second set of probabilities):

$$EV\ (S_1) = 0.857(1/2) + 0.643(3/8) + 0.429(1/8) = 0.723$$
$$EV\ (S_2) = 1.000(1/2) + 0.429(3/8) + 0(1/8) = 0.661$$

The decision-maker should select Strategy 1, which has the larger expected payoff. For this example, the objection raised before seems reasonable, and in accord with the decision-maker's utility, as measured by the standard-gamble technique. With a proper measure, there is no other rational decision criterion than the selection of that strategy associated with the largest expected payoff.

DECISION CRITERIA UNDER UNCERTAINTY

The case of decision-making under uncertainty is more complicated. For example, take the decision problem of an investor who has the objective of achieving the maximum possible rate of return. Assume that he has only three possible investments (his strategies): speculative stocks, high-grade stocks, or bonds. Further assume that only three possible states of nature can occur: war, peace, or depression. We will ignore the many nuances of capital gains, taxes on income, and so on. The investor has determined his payoffs for each of the nine possible combinations of a strategy and a state of nature. He has expressed his payoffs as rates of return on his investment and his payoff matrix looks like this:

	N_1 WAR	N_2 PEACE	N_3 DEPRESSION
S_1: Speculative stocks	20	1	−6
S_2: High-grade stocks	9	8	0
S_3: Bonds	4	4	4

Now, of course, the distinctive difference between this case and the preceding one is that the investor has no knowledge of the probabilities of the various states of nature. He has, therefore, no way to calculate an expected payoff for his strategies. What criterion should he use in selecting a strategy?

At the present time, decision theory provides no one best criterion for selecting a strategy under conditions of uncertainty. Instead, there are a number of different criteria, each of which has a perfectly good rationale to justify it. The choice among these criteria is determined by organizational policy and/or the attitude of the decision-maker. As we shall see, the use of different criteria can result in the selection of different strategies. We shall discuss only some of the suggested criteria.

CRITERION OF PESSIMISM

First, the *maximin* criterion was suggested by Abraham Wald. (The reason for the name will become clear as we proceed.) Wald suggested that the decision-maker should be completely pessimistic. He should act as if Nature would always be malevolent, i.e., for whatever strategy he selected Nature would choose a state that would minimize his payoff. Wald stated that the decision-maker should then select his strategy so that he would get as large a payoff as he could under these circumstances. Let us return to our example. If the investor selects S_1, the worst that can happen is that a depression will occur, in which case his payoff would be -6. Suppose he selected S_2. Again, the worst that could happen would be a depression, in which case he would have a payoff of 0. If he selected S_3, however, he will always get a payoff of 4, no matter what state of nature occurred. In other words, the worst that could happen to him in this case would be a payoff of 4. We can arrange these conclusions in tabular form.

STRATEGY	WORST, OR MINIMUM, PAYOFF
1	-6
2	0
3	$4\leftarrow$

Following Wald's suggestion, the best that the investor can do, assuming that Nature will always be malevolent, is to select that strategy which has the largest minimum payoff—the maximum minimum—or maximin. The largest such payoff (the maximin payoff) is 4, which the investor will get if he selects Strategy 3 and invests his money in bonds. In this *particular* case the investor will always get 4 from Strategy 3. In general, the use of this criterion will *guarantee* the manager at least as large a payoff as the maximin payoff. Sometimes, of course, a larger payoff will result. The Wald maximin criterion dictates the selection of Strategy 3—investing in bonds.

The argument based on pessimism can be described as a conservative approach to an intrinsically difficult situation. There is further elucidation of this criterion, stemming from its application to the theory of games. This will be encountered subsequently. It is also interesting to note that this is the criterion professed by the majority of adherents to the objectivist approach in probability and statistics. Bear in mind that this criterion is the sole one which can be defended rigorously if the payoffs can only be ranked.

CRITERION OF OPTIMISM

Hurwicz[2] suggested a variant of this criterion. He asks, essentially, why always assume that Nature will be malevolent? After all, we sometimes get good breaks. Suppose an optimistic decision-maker felt "lucky" in a particular case about his chances of having a good state of nature occur? How might he be rational about this feeling? First let us assume that the decision-maker is a complete optimist—the exact opposite to the Wald pessimist. He assumes that Nature will treat him kindly, selecting that state of nature which will yield the highest possible payoff for the strategy he has selected. How would he proceed? Obviously, he would look at the various payoffs for each strategy and select the largest payoff for each strategy. In our case he would find:

STRATEGY	BEST, OR MAXIMUM, PAYOFF
1	20←
2	9
3	4

Since he thinks Nature will give him the largest payoff, he will select that strategy with the largest maximum—the maximum maximum—or abbreviated, the *maximax*. In this case the maximax is the payoff of 20, which he will receive if he selects his first strategy and war occurs. (Admittedly, this makes him a strange kind of optimist.)

Now, Hurwicz didn't suggest that a rational decision-maker should be completely optimistic. He did suggest that if a decision-maker felt "lucky" or optimistic he should be able to be rational about it. For this purpose he introduced the idea of a *coefficient of optimism*. As we have seen, the complete optimist takes account only of the largest payoff for each strategy. The coefficient of optimism is a means by which the manager can take account of both the largest and the smallest payoffs —weighting their importance to his decision in accordance with his own feeling of optimism. The coefficient of optimism is defined in terms of a lottery between the largest and smallest payoffs. In other words, the decision-maker assigns to the maximum payoff a probability which he would be willing to accept in a lottery between that maximum payoff and the minimum payoff. This probability is his coefficient of opti-

[2] Leonid Hurwicz, *Optimality Criteria for Decision Making under Ignorance* (Cowles Commission discussion paper, STATISTICS, No. 370, 1951, mimeographed; cited in R. D. Luce and Howard Raiffa, *Games and Decisions* (New York: John Wiley & Sons, Inc., 1958).

mism. Suppose, for example, that our decision-maker had a coefficient of optimism of $\frac{3}{5}$. This means that he would be satisfied to accept a lottery in which the maximum payoff had a probability of occurrence of $\frac{3}{5}$ and the minimum payoff had a probability of occurrence of $\frac{2}{5}$. By Hurwicz's criterion we must determine the expected payoff of each strategy, assuming that *either* the maximum *or* the minimum will occur and with the indicated probabilities. The calculations are straightforward:

STRATEGY	MAXIMUM PAYOFF	MINIMUM PAYOFF	EXPECTED PAYOFF
1	20	−6	$20(0.6) + (−6)(0.4) = 9.6$←
2	9	0	$9(0.6) + 0(0.4) = 5.4$
3	4	4	$4(0.6) + 4(0.4) = 4.0$

According to the Hurwicz criterion, the investor should select his first strategy—investing in speculative stocks.

It may be noted that a coefficient of optimism of 1 leads to the procedure of the complete optimist, which we described above. Similarly, a coefficient of optimism of 0 leads to the Wald criterion—that of the complete pessimist. Suppose the decision-maker doesn't know his coefficient of optimism. Luce and Raiffa suggest one way to determine what it is.[3] Consider the following simple decision payoff matrix. It reflects the values of the original matrix where the payoffs have been converted to the 0-1 utility scale:

	N_1 WAR	N_3 DEPRESSION
S_1: Speculative stocks	1	0
S_4:	x	x

The new strategy S_4 has been chosen so that the payoffs will be the same no matter which state of nature occurs. For example, in the present case it might be the strategy of leaving the money in the savings bank rather than investing. The strategy S_1 contains only the *maximum* and *minimum* payoffs in the original payoff matrix. Suppose, now, that the decision-maker has a coefficient of optimism of k (an unknown which remains to be determined; we know only that, by definition, it must be at or between 0 and 1). With k as the coefficient of optimism

---

[3] Luce and Raiffa, *Games and Decisions*, p. 283.

THE ANALYSIS OF DECISIONS

the individual would calculate the expected values of the two strategies as before. In this case they are

Strategy	Expected payoff
1	k
2	x

For what value of x in the payoff matrix above would the decision-maker be indifferent between the two strategies? Note that this is really the standard-gamble technique again. Suppose the investor is indifferent between S_1 and S_4 if x has the value $\frac{1}{4}$. This means that the expected payoffs, in the Hurwicz sense, must be equal at $x = \frac{1}{4}$, or else the decision-maker wouldn't be indifferent. We conclude, then, that for this investor the coefficient of optimism, k, must be $\frac{1}{4}$.

Some say that this criterion is not as realistic as the one preceding or the two that follow this discussion. It may even be that the Hurwicz criterion is less likely to be used in practice.[4] Nevertheless, it is enriching for our discussion. First, it shows how one can attempt to include more than one payoff in the decision criterion without using all of them. Second, since it is a perfectly reasonable argument it demonstrates further variety and the difficulty of unambiguously selecting a criterion for this class of decision problem. With such variety, what does it mean to be rational in the face of uncertainty. Third, the procedure for determining the coefficient of optimism is yet another example of how one can go about obtaining quantitative measures for subjective utilities and valuations. This is such a crucial problem that any illustrations of procedures for coping with it are worthy of consideration.

CRITERION OF REGRET

A completely different criterion has been suggested by Savage.[5] This criterion requires an alternative payoff measure before it can be used. By "Savage criterion" we shall mean both the recommended payoff measure and the specific decision criterion applied to it.

We know that after a decision has been made and the state of na-

[4] There is no doubt that managers avoid decision problems under uncertainty as much as possible. They do this by ignoring the existence of such problems and by deferring these decisions. Faced with the need to reach a decision under uncertainty, knowledge of these criteria can be illuminating, but it is too much to expect them to replace intuition.

[5] Leonard J. Savage, "The Theory of Statistical Decision," *Journal of the American Statistical Association*, 46 (1951), 55-67.

ture has occurred—the decision-maker receives the (indicated) payoff. Savage argues that after he knows the outcome the decider can experience regret because, now that he knows what state of nature occurred, he may wish he had selected a different strategy. Savage maintains that the decision-maker should attempt to minimize this regret which he can experience. Exactly what is the nature of this regret? It resides in the fact that the best strategy may not have been selected for the particular state of nature that did occur. Savage suggests that the amount of regret can be measured by the difference between the payoff actually received and the payoff that could have been received if the state of nature that was going to occur had been known.

Thus, in our previous example, suppose war actually occurred. If the investor had selected his first strategy, he would experience no regret because he had already gotten the largest possible payoff. But if he had selected his second strategy he would have lost $20 - 9 = 11$, which he might otherwise have had. This measures his regret. If he had selected his third strategy he would experience regret of $20 - 4 = 16$. Now, suppose peace prevailed. If the investor had selected his second strategy he would experience no regret because he would have obtained the largest possible payoff. But if he had selected his first strategy he would experience regret of $8 - 1 = 7$. And if he had chosen his third strategy he would experience regret of $8 - 4 = 4$. If a depression occurred, the investor would experience no regret if he had selected his third strategy because it would have given him the largest possible payoff. If he had selected the first strategy, however, he would experience regret of $4 - (-6) = 10$. The selection of the second strategy in this case would give him regret of $4 - 0 = 4$. All of these measures can be conveniently presented in a *regret matrix:*

	N_1	N_2	N_3
S_1:	0	7	10
S_2:	11	0	4
S_3:	16	4	0

Savage then proposes to use a straightforward variant of the Wald criterion as the decision criterion for the regret matrix. Like Wald he, too, chooses to be completely pessimistic about the state of nature that will occur. It will always be against the individual's best interests. The variant is required because the regret matrix measures regret, which (like costs) we want to make as small as possible. The original matrix represented (profit-type) payoffs, which we want to make as large as possible. But this difference is only minor.

We ask: What is the worst that can happen to the decision-maker taking each of his strategies in turn? When we discussed the Wald criterion with respect to *profits* the answer was the minimum payoff for each strategy. Here it is the maximum regret in each row. We should note that this variant of the criterion is identical to that of the Wald criterion when applied to a cost matrix. We quickly obtain:

STRATEGY	WORST, OR MAXIMUM, REGRET
1	10←
2	11
3	16

The decision-maker can insure himself against experiencing extreme regrets by selecting the strategy that has the minimum maximum, i.e., the *minimax*. In this case the minimax regret is 10. It is the maximum regret that the decision-maker must experience, assuming he selects his first strategy, which is to invest in speculative stocks. Of course, he may experience less regret, but 10 is the most regret he can possibly experience.

One could apply a criterion other than the minimax to the regret matrix. Either the Hurwicz or the Laplace criterion (to be discussed next) could be used instead of Wald's criterion. This is why it can be said that Savage's major contribution is the regret measure of utility. Nonetheless, for us the Savage criterion will describe both the development of the regret matrix and the application of the *Wald criterion* to it.

The Savage argument is applicable to either cost or profit matrices. If the original payoff matrix is expressed in "actual" dollars (whether of profits or costs), then the Savage regret calculation is equivalent to the determination of *opportunity costs*. This is a vitally important economic concept.[6] From all perspectives, a regret matrix is an opportunity cost matrix. This suggests that the regret matrix is rooted in fundamental economic truths and this is further supported by the fact that a powerful empirical argument exists in favor of the Savage criterion. Namely, it is the only criterion that can make a "hedging" strategy optimal. Hedging is the procedure for protecting oneself

---

[6] See page 35 for a previous discussion of the opportunity cost concept.

against fluctuations in the market price of commodities. Since many businessmen hedge, we have empirical evidence of Savage's criterion in use.[7]

THE SUBJECTIVIST CRITERION

All three previous criteria operated without reference to the probabilities associated with relevant states of nature. Consequently, they are well-suited for persons who subscribe to objective interpretations of probabilities. In the investor's case, this would be a crucial issue because it is clear that the states of nature in this problem do not lend themselves to objective probability assignments. After all, these states of nature are not part of a stable and repeatable system. Hence, they are not subject to frequency counts. In contrast, the subjectivist would maintain that the manager has useful information in the form of degrees of belief concerning the likelihoods of occurrence of the relevant states of nature. For the subjectivist, this problem is just like any other decision problem under risk.

It is evident that some problems which the objectivist considers classified under uncertainty will be considered classified under risk by the subjectivist. Are many problems affected in this way? The answer is yes—a very large number. And this explains why the dispute between objectivists and subjectivists is so important. For the objectivist, a significant proportion of all decision problems (particularly those which occur at higher organizational levels) are cases of uncertainty. For the subjectivist, few decision problems exist under uncertainty. To say that a decision problem is operating under uncertainty means to the subjectivist that the administrator has absolutely no information about the likelihoods of the states of nature. Most managers would agree that such total ignorance is quite unlikely. So the subjectivist treats most decision problems as cases of risk. This has the important advantage that the decision criterion is not in dispute.

There remain decision problems under uncertainty—even for the subjectivist. We shall now consider the criterion that the subjectivist recommends in this case. It is called the Laplace criterion, and has been the subject of impassioned debate for many years.

The criterion is simple to state. Since we don't know the probabilities with which the various states of nature will transpire, we will assume that they are all equal. In other words, the inference is that every

---

[7] See Problem 5g at the end of this chapter.

state of nature is equally likely to occur. Then we calculate the expected payoff for each strategy and select that strategy which has the largest expected payoff. That is, where there are n states of nature:

$$\text{EV } (S_i) = \frac{1}{n} \sum_{j=1}^{j=n} P_{ij}$$

This is straightforward. Why all the argument about it? One of the main reasons for contention is that the assumption of equal probabilities involves a famous doctrine called the *principle of insufficient reason*. The gist of this principle is: without specific cause a particular something won't happen. The relationship of the principle of insufficient reason to the problem at hand is direct. Since we know of no reason for one state of nature to occur rather than another, we assume that one is as likely to occur as another. The principle when used in this way *in connection with probabilities* is associated with the name of the eighteenth-century English clergyman Thomas Bayes. It is Bayes' hypothesis that if we have no reason to believe one probability to be different from another—we should assume them equal.

The principle has other uses in probability theory as well, and all of them violently debated. For example, how do we know that a fair coin has a probability of ½ of showing heads when it is tossed? One answer is that we know it because of the principle of insufficient reason. There is no specific reason why the coin should come up one way rather than another, so the probabilities must be equal (hence ½, since there are only two possibilities). Many probabilists reject this argument. They state that the only reason we think the probability of a head is ½ is the fact that we have observed it come up about half the time.

One of the best-known arguments of the Middle Ages had to do with this principle of insufficient reason. Jean Buridan, in the first half of the fourteenth century, invented an imaginary ass—known ever since as Buridan's Ass. This ass was supposed to be placed exactly in the middle between two identical bales of hay. Buridan maintained that the ass must starve to death because it would have no reason to go to one bale of hay rather than another—an interesting application of the principle. Another famous ancient use of the principle was with regard to the position of the earth in space. This argument ran to the effect that the earth couldn't be just anyplace in space because, if this were the case, God would have had no reason to put it one place rather than another. Therefore, He would never have put it anywhere. Starting from here they proceeded to prove that the earth must be at the center

124 THE ANALYSIS OF DECISIONS

of the universe. Such uses of the principle as this sufficed to bring it into considerable disrepute. Nonetheless, the principle has many proponents who state that if used with caution, it is as legitimate as many other basic principles which underlie our efforts to understand the nature of reality.

The application of the subjectivist criterion is simple. Since there are three states of nature in our investor's example we assume that the probability of occurrence of each of them is $\frac{1}{3}$. On this basis we can easily calculate the expected payoff for each strategy:

STRATEGY	EXPECTED PAYOFF	
1	$\frac{1}{3}[20 + 1 + (-6)]$	$= 5$
2	$\frac{1}{3}(9 + 8 + 0)$	$= 5.67 \leftarrow$
3	$\frac{1}{3}(4 + 4 + 4)$	$= 4$

The largest expected payoff is that of Strategy 2. This is the strategy which should be selected according to the Laplace criterion.

Other decision criteria have been suggested, but these four are among the best-known ones. It is interesting to note that every strategy in our example has been selected by one of the criteria. Strategy 1 (speculative stocks) was selected by the Savage criterion and by the Hurwicz criterion with coefficient of optimism of $\frac{3}{5}$. Strategy 2 (high-grade stocks) was selected by the Laplace criterion. And Strategy 3 was selected by the Wald criterion. The selection of the decision criterion is obviously of crucial importance. So it must be emphasized that there is *no best criterion* in the sense that a conclusive argument can be offered for it. As a matter of fact, there are examples that run counter to each of the criteria. By this we mean specific decision problems for which common sense would indicate a different selection of strategy than that indicated by the decision criterion. It should not be construed, however, that common sense is the ultimate criterion. Common sense may work well enough when reality is uncomplicated. Trouble starts when significant complexity exists and common sense tells us that we can no longer rely on common sense. In such cases the choice of criterion must be left to the decision-maker. It will be determined by individual attitudes or by company policy.

A DECISION CRITERION FOR DECISION CRITERIA

A question might be raised at this point: If decision theory is so useful, why can't the problem of the decision criterion to be used be formulated as a decision problem and solved using decision theory? In other words, why not assume that the decision-maker has four available strategies (say the four criteria discussed above), determine the possible states of nature, the objective, the payoff, and establish the payoff matrix. Then use decision theory to select a strategy—*viz.*, the decision criterion to be used for decision problems.

This question involves us with the mirror problem of how to decide how to decide (previously discussed in Chapter 2). Although we cannot completely unravel this knotty problem, there are several important aspects which will be worth considering. To begin with, how can we formulate the objective which is one step removed from our previous objective—to maximize the rate of return on our investment? Of course, we still want to maximize the return but we want something else in addition. In the investment example, all three strategies, under different criteria, held promise of maximizing our return. This seems like nonsense until we recognize the fact that uncertainty cannot be compromised. *Our problem in rendering decisions under uncertainty is to do it in such a way that our attitudes and state of mind are not jeopardized.* Consequently, the formulation of our new objective must include consideration of the decisioner's personality, attitudes, and way of life. The strategies are the four decision criteria. The states of nature become the range of values which the payoff measure (rate of return) could assume. For simplicity we can call them: win, lose, and draw. The new payoff measure must be some index of the *change* that will occur *in our state of mind* for any combination of strategy and state of nature. Let's see then what we have.

We must first characterize the individuals who would use the different decision criteria. We can call them: cautious, adventurous, bad loser, and rational. There are, of course, many other types of decision-makers and all shades between them. In this characterization we are taking some obvious liberties for the purpose of emphasizing the point. The four different kinds of decision-makers would now proceed to fill in the payoff measures for the matrix below:

	WIN	DRAW	LOSE
Wald (cautious):			
Hurwicz (adventurous):			
Savage (bad loser):			
Laplace (rational):			

We can readily imagine that all four types of people will put different payoff measures into this matrix. For example, if an adventurous person decides to act cautiously and loses, he will be much more unhappy than if he had lost taking a sizable risk. The exact reverse will be true of the cautious person. The question now arises, assuming that we have filled in such a payoff matrix, how do we determine the probabilities of win, draw, and lose? Since they exist under uncertainty, we must choose a decision criterion (Wald, Hurwicz, Savage, or Laplace?), and we are back to the same problem with which we started. If we choose, we can pass on to the next mirror reflection. On the other hand, the adventurous person is likely to say: "I'm counting on luck," and he will rate "win" as more probable. The cautious person will say: "I can't count on luck," and he will lower the probability of win.

SENSITIVITY OF THE CRITERION

There is still another way of looking at this problem. We shall discard the influence of attitude and turn to the Laplace criterion, introducing small deviations from the assumption of equal probabilities. In other words, we are going to presume that we are not completely uncertain and that one of the states of nature is just a little more likely than any other state of nature. It will be recognized that even if we make small changes in all of the probabilities of the states of nature, we are no longer making decisions under uncertainty. We are now deciding under risk. Yet, if the changes that we have made are small, the formulation is almost identical with the Laplace criterion. At some point, as we add little increments to the probability of one particular state of nature, while taking away an equivalent amount from the other probabilities, the strategy chosen by the Laplace criterion will be replaced by another strategy which has a larger expected value for the payoff. The extent of change required to achieve such a shift reflects upon the sensitivity of this aspect of the system.

For example, the Laplace selection of Strategy 2 in the investment problem shifts to the selection of Strategy 1 when the first state of nature (war) goes from 0.33 probability to 0.37. (The other two states of nature are changed from 0.33 to 0.31.) On the other hand, the probability of depression must increase from 0.33 to 0.53 for Strategy 2 to shift to Strategy 3 (while war and peace go from 0.33 to 0.23). One way to interpret this is to say that if Strategy 1 is chosen by a particular criterion—except the Laplace—that criterion was chosen by the decision-maker because he had more knowledge than he was aware he had. That is why he chose a criterion other than the Laplace. In fact, he believed that war was more likely than peace or depression by an amount of 0.04. The required shift is small, and thereby the system is sensitive to minor attitudinal biases which support the contention that war will occur. Similarly, if the decision-maker's criterion selected Strategy 3 then we infer that he had reason to believe that a depression would occur and that he had as much as 0.20 additional belief in this outcome. This required shift is large. The system is insensitive to minor biases that a depression will occur.

The approach we are using is *sensitivity probing*, which is based on the question: How unbalanced must the relative uncertainties be before we stop calling them uncertainties? Since if we knew the probabilities of the states of nature we would use expected values, the Laplace criterion is the only one (of our four) that expresses *no attitude* except the desire to be rational. That is, if we say we don't know the probabilities then we must act as if we don't know the probabilities. That is why we characterize the Laplace criterion as rational. Therefore, the following observations about the attitude of the decision-maker seem relevant to the selection of the decision criterion.

1. States of nature may be equiprobable but it is unlikely that the individual has the chances of their occurring equally weighted *in his mind*.

2. It is possible that if you choose a criterion other than Laplace it is because you favor the probability that one or another state of nature will prevail. In any case, when it seems desirable, the Laplace criterion can permit the individual to think of the states of nature in equiprobable terms. Sensitivity testing can shed some light on the degree to which attitudes may affect results.

DECISIONS UNDER CONFLICT

All previous discussion has been in terms of decisions against Nature. The basic supposition has been that the state of nature which occurs will be independent of the selection of strategy of the manager. When rational opponents are involved, we have decisions under conflict and this supposition is no longer true. On the contrary, usually the rational opponent (or opponents) will give careful thought to what the decision-maker can be expected to do before selecting his (or their) own courses of action. The essence of decision problems involving rational opponents is conflict of interest. For our discussion, the various opponents are all presumed to be rational. Therefore, they will be attempting to frustrate their opponents' wishes. As will be shown, if one opponent exhibits nonrational behavior, he can only suffer for it.

This part of decision theory is commonly known as game theory. It relates to a complex, highly developed body of knowledge. Games (in the general sense of game theory) are customarily classified according to the number of opponents and the degree of conflict of interest. The theory of games with only two opponents presents one of the simplest (but not simple!) cases. It is the variant most thoroughly developed. We shall confine our attention to this kind of game.

Games that have complete conflict of interest are ones in which what one opponent gains, the other loses. These are called *zero-sum games*. The nearest approximation to this kind of game in the business world would be a competitive battle for share of the market. One competitor can only increase his *share* of the market at the expense of his competitors. Political parties vying for Congressional seats is another illustration. Competitions for the award of fixed grants from foundations and for larger shares of a given budget also apply. Most recreational games that we play for fun are of this completely competitive type.

Games with less than complete conflict of interest are called *non-zero-sum games*. The majority of organization problems involving rational opponents are of this type. An example would be a competitive battle for sales. Here the *size* of the market is involved. An advertising campaign might result in an increased share of the market, but it could also benefit the other competitors because of the tendency of advertising to stimulate sales for the product as well as for the brand. In other words, the gain of one competitor in terms of sales volume is not necessarily completely at the expense of the other competitors. The same reasoning applies to military conflicts and to conflicts between individuals and groups within and between organizations (see pp. 57-58). The theory of nonzero-sum games is fascinating, but too elaborate for discussion here. We shall confine our attention to *two-person, zero-sum games* and the explanation of the decision criterion that is appropriate for this case.

Our concern is with competitive actions on the part of the opponent rather than with states of nature. So, instead of the N's we have been using we will use C's to represent the various possible competitive strategies. Since what one competitor wins, another loses (in a zero-sum game), we can use one payoff matrix as before to represent the decision problem. We could not do this for a nonzero-sum game. In order to analyze nonzero-sum games we need a separate payoff matrix for each opponent.

Let us take as an example a decision problem involving a struggle for the share of the market against one opponent. Suppose that the manager has three strategies available and his competitor has four (there is no need for them to have the same number of possible strategies). The payoff matrix will be constructed in terms of the percentage-points increase in market share accruing to the manager.

		OPPONENT'S STRATEGIES			
		C_1	C_2	C_3	C_4
	S_1:	0.6	−0.3	1.5	−1.1
MANAGER'S	S_2:	0.7	0.1	0.9	0.5
STRATEGIES	S_3:	−0.3	0.0	−0.5	0.8

This payoff matrix is read in exactly the same way as were the earlier ones. If the manager selects his first strategy and his opponent selects his third strategy, then the manager will increase his share of the market by 1.5 percentage points. And, of course, since this is a zero-sum game, the competitor will *lose* 1.5 percentage points of the market. Negative entries represent losses to the manager and gains to the competitor. The question is: How should the manager select his strategy? The difference from the cases where there was no rational opponent is that now, in reaching his decision, the manager must take into account what the opponent is likely to do. And, of course, vice versa holds.

It might appear that this would greatly increase the complexity of the decision problem and require some new kind of decision criterion. Actually, that isn't the case. In this kind of game it can be shown that the *only* rational decision criterion is the *Wald criterion*. Let us go through the reasoning to determine the strategy to be selected by using this criterion and then attempt to justify our statement that it is the *only* rational criterion. The manager reasons, according to the Wald criterion, that if he selects S_1 he might lose as much as 1.1 (if his opponent selects C_4). If he selects S_2 he cannot do worse than to gain 0.1 (if his opponent selects C_2). If the manager selects S_3 he may lose 0.5 (if his opponent chooses C_3). Thus:

STRATEGY	MINIMUM PAYOFF
S_1	−1.1
S_2	0.1←
S_3	−0.5

Following the Wald criterion we now select the maximum of these minimum payoffs, the *maximin*. In this case it is 0.1, resulting from selecting S_2—which should therefore be the choice.

Remember, the opponent is rational. What is he thinking? He, too, elects to use the Wald criterion. From his standpoint the worst that can happen if he selects C_1 is that he will lose 0.7 (the maximum value in the column since the payoffs are in terms of *his opponent*). If he selects C_2 the worst that can happen is that he should lose 0.1 (if his opponent selects S_2). Proceeding similarly we obtain:

COMPETITOR'S ACTION	MAXIMUM LOSS
C_1	0.7
C_2	0.1←
C_3	1.5
C_4	0.8

According to the Wald criterion, the competitor will want to minimize his maximum loss, *the minimax* value. This minimax value is 0.1, achieved by selecting C_2. This, then, should be his choice. Thus, the best decisions on the part of the two competitors are that the manager should select S_2, his competitor should select C_2, and the result will be an increase of 0.1 percentage points in market share to the manager.

Why can we say that this is the only *rational* approach to such a competitive decision problem? Consider the situation from the standpoint of the manager. He knows that his opponent can minimize his maximum loss by selecting C_2. Assume that the opponent uses C_2. Then if the manager selected any other strategy but his S_2, he would do worse than he would by selecting S_2. If he selected S_1 he would lose 0.3 instead of winning 0.1. If he selected S_3 he would gain nothing instead of gaining 0.1. Similarly, the competitor knows that the manager can maximize his minimum gain by selecting S_2. If he does so the opponent does best by selecting his C_2. If he does anything else he loses more. Thus, with complete conflict of interest, the opponents are driven to use the Wald criterion.

If the manager knows that his competitor will not use C_2, or if he has any other pertinent information about what his competitor will do —other than what is expected of him—he will establish probabilities for the competitive strategies. From these, he can determine his own optimum strategy on the basis of decision-making under risk. In such an event, the information he has obtained has measurable utility. It will permit him to realize a greater payoff than he could otherwise expect. On the other hand, if he is unsure of his information he can continue to use his maximin strategy and *gain the advantage which must come to him if his competitor does not act in an entirely rational manner.*

It may be noted that in this payoff matrix the maximin value for the manager equaled the minimax value for his opponent—both of them being 0.1. This is by no means always the case. When the two values are different it develops that the use of *mixed strategies*—where the specific strategy to be used is selected randomly with a determined probability—will make them equal.[8] The proof of this fact is called the *fundamental theorem* of game theory. We shall not discuss this theorem further. It does not affect the point that the existence of a rational opponent can simplify the decision problem.

Frequently, the information required to construct a payoff matrix is difficult to obtain. This may be especially true when the payoffs must represent the utilities of various outcomes to both participants in a competitive decision system. We have recourse, however, to the use of ranked data as illustrated in the following example. A lock manufacturer makes replacement parts for items that the company no longer produces. In addition, the company makes a new line of locks which must carry the cost of the replacement business. It has always been this firm's policy to carry stock on obsolete models because of the belief that it creates goodwill. However, if the company charged the proper amount to make a profit or just break even on replacement parts, the cost of these parts would be so exorbitant that it would defeat the purpose of improving goodwill. The company now learns that a competitor is considering the possibility of manufacturing the entire line of replacement parts. As a result, the appropriate decision problem is formulated. There are three possible strategies and two states of nature. The sales manager of the company determines the outcomes as follows:

	N_1	N_2
S_1:	O_{11}	O_{12}
S_2:	O_{21}	O_{22}
S_3:	O_{31}	O_{32}

S_1: continue making replacements.

S_2: announce suspension of the policy to make replacements to become effective at some date in the far future.

[8] The equal value is called a *saddlepoint,* whether it arises from mixed or pure strategies.

S_3: stop making replacements.

N_1: competitor decides to make replacement parts.

N_2: competitor decides not to make replacement parts.

O_{11}: we lose some replacement customers—but gain some new customers since the competitor's prices on his new line must go up to absorb the cost of replacement parts.

O_{12}: we lose no replacement customers—but we gain fewer new customers (present policy).

O_{21}: we lose more replacement customers than in O_{11}—but we gain about the same number of new customers as in O_{11}.

O_{22}: we lose fewer replacement customers than in O_{11}—and we gain fewer new customers as in O_{12}.

O_{31}: we lose all our replacement customers—and we gain more new customers than in O_{11}.

O_{32}: we lose more replacement customers than in O_{21}—and we gain fewer new customers than in O_{31}.

These outcomes can be further simplified by a logical analysis of the statements. This produces the following:

O_{11}: lose x gain y
O_{12}: lose 0   gain $y - a$
O_{21}: lose $x + b$ gain y
O_{22}: lose $x - c$ gain $y - a$
O_{31}: lose all   gain $y + c$
O_{32}: lose $x + b + d$ gain $y + c - e$

If the sales manager can put in values appropriate to the gains and losses, he can then quantitatively solve this decision problem. However, if he cannot supply numbers, he can rank the outcomes according to his best judgment. Let us assume that he has ranked the outcomes with the numbers that appear in the payoff matrix below. (1 represents the poorest payoff; 6 represents the best payoff.)

	N_1	N_2	MINIMUM PAYOFF
S_1:	4	6	4**
S_2:	3	5	3
S_3:	1	2	1
MAXIMUM PAYOFF:	4*	6	

If we now apply the maximin (**) and the minimax (*) criteria, we find that the company will do best to continue on its present policy. We can also observe that if the competitor has the same approximate

utility as the sales manager, and derives approximately the same estimates for the payoffs, he will begin to manufacture replacement parts.
If the competitor does not have the same approximate utility then
a nonzero-sum game with two payoff matrices is required. And even
this assumes that each opponent is able to estimate his competitor's
utilities.

Some examples of how nonzero-sum games can arise were given
above. The common reason for competitive situations being nonzero-
sum games is that the utilities of the opponents are not the same. Since
utilities are, by definition, subjective, it may well be that the opponents
do not know the utilities of their competitors for the various outcomes.
As a matter of fact, one might expect that this would be the usual case.
Since certain types of organizations often have some degree of similarity in goals, we would expect that the opponents might have some idea
of the opposition's utility for the various outcomes. However, if a decision problem arose in which the administrator really had no idea
about the utility his opponent ascribed to the outcomes, then the decision problem would have to be treated under uncertainty. This results
because, not knowing the utilities of his opponent for the outcomes, the
decision-maker has no way of knowing anything about the probabilities of the different competitive actions—which is an equivalent definition of decision-making under uncertainty.

In terms of actual organizational conditions, which decision problems are most likely to arise? It is clear that a large number of decision
problems are primarily involved with states of nature. So the usefulness
of our analysis concerning certainty, risk, and uncertainty is evident.
But what about rational opponents? According to the classical conditions of *free enterprise* any decision problem is simply against nature
because, by the definition of these conditions, no one business can have
any effect on market conditions through any strategy which it might
elect to follow. On the other hand, wherever free-enterprise conditions
do not exist in a specific market we are obliged to include competitive
actions as part of the decision problem. In short, under *oligopolistic*
conditions in a particular market it is necessary to include competitive
actions in the payoff matrix. Also, many problems of a monopoly can
be construed as games against a rational opponent. In this case, they
are the suppliers and consumers. Generally, small organizations that
deal in a large marketplace can ignore the effects of a rational opponent. This puts them in the position of deciding under conditions of
risk or uncertainty. As the size of the company increases with respect
to the market, the influence of rational opponents is felt. As a rule, a

particular management can evaluate its situation with respect to the importance of competition.

PROBLEMS

1. A drugstore chain has six stores. A new company policy is established which, in effect, will reassign the present six store managers to the stores in such a way as to minimize the total traveling time of the managers from home to store. How many possible arrangements (strategies) are there? Why is this decision-making under certainty?

2. A department store has four different strategies for obtaining advance information about the line of merchandise which their chief competitor will carry in the next season. The amount of information that can be obtained will depend on whether or not the competitor is aware that the department store is trying to get this information. Assume the following payoff matrix:

	N_1	N_2
S_1:	-4	10
S_2:	2	2
S_3:	3	0
S_4:	-1	6

where N_1 = competitor is aware,
    N_2 = competitor isn't aware,
payoff measures are the utility of information obtained, and negative values represent misinformation.

   a. If the competitor is aware (state of nature N_1), what strategy should be chosen?
   b. If the competitor is not aware (state of nature N_2), what strategy should be chosen?
   c. Assume that the probabilities are 0.90 for N_1 and 0.10 for N_2. What choice should be made?
   d. What would be the maximin choice?
   e. What would be the maximax choice?
   f. Assume a coefficient of optimism of 0.70. Which strategy will be chosen? Now, assume a coefficient of pessimism of 0.70. Does the choice of strategy change?
   g. What would be the result if we took the minimax of regret?
   h. What would be the result if we use the principle of insufficient reason?

3. Assume that the boxes of a tic-tac-toe game are numbered 1-9. How many possible combinations of the numbers (strategies) are available to the player who begins the game? How many are available to the second

player? How many boxes are there in the payoff matrix? Ignoring the numbers of the boxes, how many basically different opening moves are there? How many basically different second moves are there? How large would the payoff matrix be for the first two moves?

4. Instead of tic-tac-toe boxes, consider each number to represent a sales area. Assume that whichever company gets to an area first wins that area. Each company has only one salesman. The salesman must spend one day in each area in order to win it for his company. Say that every move of one box along a row or column takes one day traveling time. Every move of one box along a diagonal takes two days traveling time. Can you devise a game to fit these rules? What would be each player's objective?

5. You are working as a consultant in a foreign country where the exchange rate is 100 units of the foreign currency for $1. You will be there for five months and your expenses are fixed in units of the foreign currency at 50,000 units per month. A sky-rocketing inflation is temporarily in check while the government is attempting to negotiate a large loan. If the government gets the loan the effect will be to lower the exchange rate by 10 per cent. If the loan is refused the exchange rate will increase by 20 per cent. In addition, a general strike has been called. If this strike is successful the government will be forced to take some economic measures which will increase the exchange rate by 15 per cent. If the strike fails the rate will decrease by 10 per cent. It can be assumed that the two events in question (loan and strike) are independent. Thus there are four states of nature:

N_1: Loan, strike fails, rate drops to 81.0
N_2: Loan, strike succeeds, rate increases to 103.5
N_3: No loan, strike fails, rate increases to 108.0
N_4: No loan, strike succeeds, rate increases to 138.0

For our purposes it will be sufficient to consider three strategies:

S_1: Immediately convert enough dollars into foreign units to meet all five months' expenses.
S_2: Wait until the events above have occurred, meanwhile holding dollars.
S_3: Hedge by converting half the amount now and holding half in dollars.

Your objective will be to minimize your dollar expenses.

a. Determine the payoff matrix in dollars of expense.
b. What is the minimax strategy?
c. What is the optimal strategy if the coefficient of optimism is 0.6?
d. What is the optimal strategy by the criterion of minimization of regret?
e. What is the optimal strategy by the Laplace criterion?
f. Suppose it is known that the probability that the government will receive the loan is 0.75 and the probability that the strike will succeed is 0.4. What is the optimal strategy?

g. S_3 is the hedging strategy. Show that no hedging strategy (involving the immediate conversion of a proportion k and holding $1 - k$) could be optimal under any criterion we have covered other than the Savage criterion.

h. Can you find an argument suggesting an optimal hedge in the sense of the optimal proportion k to convert now?

6. You are at a horse race and are considering placing a bet on a specific horse in a specific race. Thus, there are four possible strategies and four states of nature. Suppose the payoff matrix is:

	WIN	PLACE	SHOW	LOSE
BET WIN	7	−2	−2	−2
BET PLACE	3	3	−2	−2
BET SHOW	2	2	2	−2
DON'T BET	0	0	0	0

a. What is the maximin strategy?

b. What strategy is selected by the Hurwicz criterion with coefficient of optimism .5?

c. What strategy is selected by the Savage criterion?

d. What strategy is selected by the Laplace criterion?

e. Suppose there are eight horses in the race. Criticize the assumptions underlying the Laplace criterion and solve the decision problem under risk, which results for the above payoff matrix on the basis of your criticism.

f. What might be the subjectivist's answer to your criticism in "e"?

7. Write down the payoff matrices for the investment problem, the lottery problem, and the numbers game problem of Chapter 4 (problems 2, 9, and 10, respectively). Apply the Wald, Savage, and Laplace criteria to these decision problems.

8. The lock manufacturer in this chapter (p. 131f) decided, on the basis of ranked estimates, to continue manufacturing replacement parts. His competitor, on the other hand, went through the same reasoning process but obtained numerical estimates, as follows: $x = y/2 = 2a = 4b = 6c = 8d = 10e$. The total replacement market $= 100x$.
What conclusion did the competitor reach?

9. As an example of some of the difficulties involved in the analysis of two-person nonzero-sum games we can use the following:

	A'S PAYOFFS				B'S PAYOFFS	
	B_1	B_2			B_1	B_2
A_1	1	−4		A_1	1	5
A_2	5	−2		A_2	−4	−2

a. What are the players' maximin strategies? Should they use them?

b. Consider the difference if the game is only played once or if it is going to be played a number of times.

c. Consider the difference if communication is allowed between the players before the game is played.

d. Suppose A and B are competitors and the first strategy in each case is to leave price unchanged. The second strategy is to lower price. Do you think payoff matrices such as these might be reasonable representations of this situation?

6 | Applied Decision Theory

Let us presume that the manager has been convinced by the preceding five chapters and that he is now prepared to put decision theory to the test of practice. He is aware that many problems will stand in his way. These difficulties in applying decision theory would eliminate many, if not most, important applications if the manager were left to his own resources. Fortunately, however, operations research (O.R.) can act in his behalf. And it is our thesis that when O.R. is considered as an adjunct to the applications of decision theory it can be best understood.

DEFINITION OF OPERATIONS RESEARCH

What, then, is operations research? In common with many other fields, it is easy to point to but hard to define. It is generally known that O.R. originated during World War II in the form of attempts by various kinds of scientists to solve military problems, which were often totally unconnected in substance with the specialties of the scientists. The O.R. approach was extended to business applications after the war, and has since become a burgeoning field with important implications and effects for industrial, institutional, and governmental systems. It has many consultants, active professional societies, thousands of books, monographs, and journals. Executive programs in O.R. and courses of study in colleges and universities abound. The steady growth in the number of practitioners is well beyond expectation. Yet, no single, generally accepted definition of what operations research is exists.

There are three main categories of definitions. First, those which are variants or elaborations of the definition proposed by Morse and Kimball:[1]

Operations research is a scientific method of providing executive departments with a quantitative basis for decisions regarding the operations under their control.

Any O.R. practitioner will recognize that much of his work falls within the compass of this description; nevertheless, it is not suitable. Replace "operations research" with "cost accounting" in the above definition and the new statement holds equally well. Or, replace "operations research" with "the control chart." The description still holds. We see that this definition does not distinguish O.R. from a number of other methodological approaches to organizational problems, some of which have been in use for a longer time than O.R. A definition that does not clearly distinguish one field from related or different fields cannot be satisfactory.

A second approach to the problem of defining O.R. is to list the various techniques that have come to be associated with it. Many descriptions of the subject proceed by listing seriatim such methodological areas as queuing theory, inventory theory, linear programming, Monte Carlo, search theory, and so on. Certainly operations research often utilizes these techniques, but to define O.R. in terms of them is a mistake. It would be like defining medicine in terms of the collection of drugs and techniques which doctors use to cure their patients. This approach to definition is obviously ridiculous for medicine, and equally so for operations research. If there is no more unity to O.R. than the latest catalogue of techniques that can be culled from the literature, then there is no merit in giving it a name.

Third, Philip Morse (who collaborated on the first definition) has whimsically suggested that O.R. *is* what O.R. practitioners *do*. This definition has the undoubted merit of being correct; but it also suffers from the equally undoubted demerit of being uninformative. We cannot use it to communicate—even among those who use it.

The approach that this book takes is that *O.R. is applied decision theory*. Operations research requires the use of scientific, mathematical, or logical means to structure and resolve *decision problems*. Construction of an adequate decision model is crucial. Questions of strategy

[1] Philip M. Morse and George E. Kimball, *Methods of Operations Research* (New York: John Wiley & Sons, Inc., 1951), p. 1.

development, recognition of states of nature, competitive considerations, outcomes and utilities, etc. are not just matters of tools and techniques. Implementation abilities for the decisions reached are implicit requirements for model construction. This is the decision context that enables a manager to better achieve a thoroughgoing rationality in dealing with his problems. With this in mind, let us examine some of the contributions that O.R. can make to the resolution of decision problems.

O.R. APPLICATIONS TO DECISION THEORY

To begin with, there is a problem in formulating objectives. Multiple objectives, conflicts between objectives, the treatment of constraints, and the effects of suboptimization are some of the difficulties normally encountered. There are, of course, a considerable number of decision situations for which these complications are not critical. In all cases, the identification and choice of objectives begins as a managerial function. Operations research can provide both stimulation and guidance, but there is no way of replacing the administrative responsibility for the clear definition of objectives. Where complex cases, including confliction, exist, O.R. can sometimes help to unravel the tangled skein of objectives.

Even when the objectives have been stated, it is not always an easy matter to discover the appropriate measures of utility. We have treated this topic at some length in Chapter 4. At that point, a number of possibilities were examined, including the use of *logarithms* as utility measures for "natural" payoffs. We also considered *ranking* and the *standard gamble* for payoffs that lack a natural measure. Problems of measurement concern every scientific field. Applied decision theory or O.R. is no exception. As needed, methods must be developed or borrowed for the observation, measurement, and construction of meaningful payoffs. Some help is available from the literature of other sciences (i.e., the behavioral and physical sciences). But this does not begin to exhaust the measurement and accounting problems that remain in the management sciences.

USING O.R. TO DISCOVER STRATEGIES, STATES OF NATURE, AND COMPETITIVE STRATEGIES

The discovery and enumeration of strategies, states of nature, and competitive strategies requires experience and imagination on the part of both the manager and the O.R. practitioner. In the section on maximization principles in Chapter 2, point two stated that all variables pertinent to the attainment of the objectives should be isolated. These variables are the components that when taken together form strategies, states of nature, and competitive strategies. But what happens when the variables that determine the outcome are not known? What can operations research methods contribute?

Not directly, but as a by-product of its logic, O.R. has been successful in helping the manager discover relevant variables. The operations research contribution to discovery has been so considerable that there has been an observable tendency to define the methodology of operations research in terms of this discovery function. While the overemphasis is unfortunate, nevertheless, the discovery attribute characterizes the generalist, and as we have previously stated, O.R. is a generalist's specialty.

A difference should be noted between the discovery of abstract variables (such as resources, activities, origins, and destinations) and the discovery of nonabstract variables that apply to specific "real-world" problems. The ability to convert from one level to the other requires the fullest coordination between O.R. and the manager. Frequently, an O.R. practitioner endeavors to discover the relevant factors for his problem by analogy with problems in different areas, such as physics, engineering, biology, or ecology. This approach demands wide experience in different fields and the ability to think *creatively* about them. Successes in this area often can be attributed to strong analogies, which stem from a similarity of verbs. Let us consider "search." A personnel department searches for new employees, an advertising campaign is a search for new customers, a plane searches for submarines or people lost at sea, a scientist searches the literature for a fact, and science searches for *true* hypotheses. Success in determining the relevant variables and their relationships in any one area may be extendible to others, with some suitable translation of terms. The verb "decide" is an excellent example in its own right. In this book we have been discussing the verb concept, "decide," in great depth, without requiring specific details to picture any one situation. Similar examples are to "allocate," "replace," and "store." By finding key verbs such as these, the practitioner may be led to a suitable, and already developed, analogy in another field.

The methods by which relevant variables and their relationships are discovered must be supported with keen perception, understanding of the system, and creative insights. These attributes are not the exclusive properties of any field. They belong to scientists and managers alike. O.R.'s particular contribution to these endeavors lies in the systematization of pattern formation and the subsequent logical analysis of meaningful analogies. For example, the variables of epidemic models that describe the spread of contagious diseases can be systematically compared with those variables that describe the sales growth of a new product. The variables of addiction models can be transformed to portray the nature of brand loyalty. Prey-predator models of ecology highlight a set of variables that might be applicable to brand share analyses. Gas laws that describe the diffusion of particles may focus attention on a proper set of variables and relations for advertising a new idea or conversely for squelching a fast-spreading rumor.[2]

On the other hand, analogies can be *deceptive*. There are numerous examples of cases where a seemingly "almost perfect" fit has led to erroneous conclusions. Sometimes it is hard to resist forcing a problem to fit an analogous technique (à la Procrustes who compulsively made everyone fit his bed—the too short were stretched and the too long were cut down to size). There are also problems for which no suitable analogies are known. Under pressure, force fits may be resorted to, but not without obvious dangers. Somehow, new forms must be found. The usefulness and cost of employing varying degrees of approximations to reality merit attention. Although we can't say much about the nature of analogic innovation, it is certain that a great deal of study concerning such creativity and the search for knowledge remains to be accomplished. All fields of endeavor share responsibility and concern in the pursuit of such progress.

USING O.R. TO HANDLE EXCESSIVE NUMBERS
OF STRATEGIES AND STATES OF NATURE

A decision concerning inventory levels might include the full range of possibilities—from stockpiling several years' supply to operating on an order-as-you-go basis with virtually no inventory on hand. Perhaps thousands or millions of possible strategies are required to represent this situation. Similarly, the complex decision of allocating an organization's resources may easily require an astronomical number of strategies to include all feasible alternatives. We noted earlier that a machine-shop problem, of no apparent complexity, could involve 2.5 quintillion strategies. A sane manager is not going to seriously consider

---

[2] See Problem 1g at the end of this chapter for further explanation.

writing out a payoff matrix involving an incredible number of rows—
no matter how enthusiastic he may be about decision theory.

In the same way, the decision-maker will often find that the number
of possible states of nature is prohibitively enormous. For example, the
relevant states of nature might include ten different levels of gross national product, ten kinds of weather, ten different situations regarding
interest rates and the availability of credit, twenty competitive strategies, five international situations, and ten possible levels of demand.
For many problems this is not unreasonably exorbitant. Yet it already
adds up to 1,000,000 ($10 \times 10 \times 10 \times 20 \times 5 \times 10$) different states of
nature. At one second per column it would take more than 11 days of
continuous work to write down these 1,000,000 columns!

How does O.R. help when there are such huge numbers of strategies
and states of nature? Whether the excessive number is attributable to
strategies, states of nature, or both, the difficulty of size is susceptible
to the same treatment—mathematical representation. By using mathematical models the enormous number of strategies and/or states of
nature can often, *but not always*, be subsumed by a few equations. When
this can be done the great number of strategies and states of nature no
longer represent an insurmountable difficulty. In the past two decades,
the capability for solving even large systems of equations has been
tremendously enhanced by the development and proliferation of large-
scale computers. Third generation computers turn out in a few days
what would formerly have been years of analysis. These computers can
solve huge systems of equations, and it is becoming increasingly feasible to represent extremely complex decision problems in mathematical
form. Before the advent of powerful computers decision problems could
sometimes be represented by equations, but these equations could not
be solved. We have come a long way on both counts.

Of course, computers must be fed the information they use. This includes careful instructions (the *program*) concerning how to perform
the appropriate operations on the information. The *program*, in turn,
is an appropriate transformation of the relevant *decision model*. Computers can be programmed for a variety of problem-solving and decision-making operations, but not until the model has been built. If a
model does not exist for the solution of a particular problem it must be
developed. This may take a great deal of time and money. However, as
more analogies are found, techniques developed, and standard programs
created, it has become possible to adapt this "library" for effective use
at much less cost.

The operations a computer can perform are basically quite simple.

For example, it can search for information that is stored in its memory; it can compare two numbers, accepting or rejecting the larger or the smaller; it can combine two numbers and thus perform addition, and so on. Computer programs are combinations of these simple operations, but the combinations are ingeniously chosen so that the result can yield complex mathematical analyses. Thanks to developments such as these, excessive numbers of strategies and states of nature are no longer *so* serious a handicap in the resolution of complex decision situations.

USING O.R. TO DETERMINE OUTCOMES

A major problem facing the manager who endeavors to use decision theory is the difficulty of determining the "actual" outcomes. At the intersection of every strategy (row) and state of nature (column) there is an outcome cell. Into this cell the manager must insert the appropriate payoff measure—which is not necessarily the natural measure of the outcome.

We have emphasized the necessity of determining the payoff *utility* that will result from a given *measured* outcome. Also, we have explained methods by which the manager can express his *utility* quantitatively for the various *outcomes*. But there remains the question: How is the *outcome* determined?

The word "determined" has two implications. In one sense it means: The *process* by which the selected strategy interacts with the state of nature that occurs to produce a specific outcome. In the other sense it means: The *knowledge* of what that outcome is. These two aspects are totally related of course. Specifically, if we know the first, we can *often* determine the second. The reader might think we should have said, "We can *always* determine the second." It would appear that if we know the process by which the strategy and the state of nature interact to produce the outcome, then we should certainly be able to determine the outcome. But a difficulty can arise.

We may not be able to solve the equations that describe the interaction (which is why we must say often instead of always). Further, even if we don't know the way in which the outcome is produced we may be able to know what it is. Sometimes this can be achieved through the analysis of past experience. For example, the meteorologist believes he knows the way various factors work to determine weather. Unfortunately, he cannot solve the equations that describe their interactions—and present-day computing equipment doesn't help. Nonetheless, he can do a pretty good job of predicting the path of a hurricane based upon the careful study and generalization of past events.

Another approach for deriving outcomes when the process is unknown is the use of *experimental* methods. The chemist may not understand the reaction between two solutions or the nature of a catalyst, but he can find out what happens in his laboratory when the two solutions are mixed or the catalyst is present. Similarly, although the consumer's mind may be a black box to the marketing manager, test markets and surveys are his laboratory for discovering outcomes in spite of his ignorance of the process from which these outcomes arise.

When the process that produces the outcomes is known, O.R. can usually bring to bear powerful mathematical tools to determine the specific outcomes. In fact, the determination of outcomes is an area in which operations research has made another major contribution. Let us look at some simple organization problems in this context.

Consider a manager in charge of some customer service system like toll booths at a bridge, operators at a switchboard, nurses in a hospital, or waiters in a restaurant. The manager has the problem of determining the number of personnel to have on duty to meet the demand. In decision-theory terms his available strategies consist of the different numbers of personnel he could assign. The states of nature will include the various possible levels of demand. Now, whatever the objectives may be, how do the given number of personnel (specific strategy) interact with the given level of demand (a particular state of nature) to produce an outcome? This is a question of process—then, what outcomes are produced? It turns out that the process by which these two variables interact is by no means obvious. Rather surprising results— quite contrary to common sense—emerge. In other words, in this decision problem, the ability to determine the outcomes is the crucial issue.

Consider an executive who must set the price for a new product. What outcome results for a specific price and a given potential demand curve (one of the states of nature) is a question dealt with by economic theory. However, it is by no means easy to apply this model to an actual situation. O.R. must be able to supply these outcomes in an empirically satisfying fashion. Now, consider a decision problem involving inventory level where the objective is to minimize total cost. As the inventory level is increased, carrying costs will increase—storage charges, depreciation costs, loss of interest on capital, and so on. Some costs, however, will decrease as the inventory level is increased—out of stock costs, expediting costs, loss of customer goodwill, and others. For any given level of inventory, higher demand implies a greater risk of losing sales; lower demand implies a greater risk of incurring overstock costs. With rising prices, a large inventory is advantageous—and vice versa with falling prices. These are only some of the factors affecting the cost minimization. So it is evidently not a simple matter to understand the system. In this case, O.R. makes use of straightforward mathematical methods which succeed in determining outcomes at a reasonable cost.

The situations described above are typical of a large number of decision problems in which the determination of the outcome is one of the major difficulties. Fortunately, even when the relationship cannot be worked out formally, there is still the possibility of using statistical and experimental methods.

USING O.R. TO MAKE A DECISION

Assume that the payoff matrix for a *large* problem has been completed. Undoubtedly, it would not exist in expanded form on paper. Rather, it would be condensed by mathematical equations. They would represent the payoff measures of all relevant strategies with all possible states of nature. The manager must now apply his selected *decision criterion* to the *mathematical representation* of the payoff matrix. The essence of the problem is to be able to search and manipulate—according to the decision criterion—billions, quintillions, decillions, or even more payoff measures. Operations research has methods available for accomplishing this feat under many different circumstances.

In summary, O.R. is an absolute necessity for the manager who wants to use decision theory as more than a toy. There are basically four ways in which O.R. provides assistance.

1. By the use of mathematical representation, large numbers of strategies and states of nature can be handled. Without such representation the *limitations* imposed by *bounded rationality* apply.
2. When the manager does not know the important variables, operations-research methods can help him discover them.
3. When the manager *does know* the important variables but does not know how to relate them to each other, to the outcome, and to the payoff measure, O.R. can sometimes provide the necessary framework.
4. The manager cannot use primitive search techniques if an innu-

merable number of payoff measures exist. Therefore, in order to apply his decision criterion, he must turn to see if mathematical methods can be devised to do this for him.

Each of the above points represents model-building under various circumstances and for different purposes. The applied decision (O.R.) approach has both weaknesses and strengths. It is in those problem areas where the executive knows that his intuition is likely to fail him that O.R. holds forth the greatest promise. Situations of great complexity will many times yield under mathematical analysis and may, in fact, become quite simple. A key to executive confusion lies in the human inability to search through millions or billions of combinations for a particular effect. On the other hand, intuition becomes more attractive as the number of relevant variables and complex relations between them increases. The efforts required to build models for increasingly complex cases frequently goes up faster than the advantages to be gained vis-à-vis intuition. Then, without trying to capture every nuance, O.R. can serve as a guide. It can audit the consultant's function in a firm (including its own) and provide management with a new source of perspective.

PROBLEMS

1. The best way to gain an appreciation of the advantages and difficulties of the use of analogies from other fields in solving organizational problems is to try and think one's way through some of them. Here is an assortment —with no promise that they are actually useful:

   a. The number of possible relationships between pairs of people increases rapidly with the total number of people. Precisely, if there are N people then there are $N(N-1)/2$ pairs. Thus, with three people $(A, B,$ and $C)$ there are three pairs $(3 \times 2)/2 = 3)$: AB, AC, and BC. Does this have any implications in terms of managing or supervising?

   b. When physical bodies grow larger the relationship of surface area to volume changes. As an approximation, volume changes as the 3/2 power of the surface area. For example, when surface area increases 4 times volume will increase $4^{3/2} = 8$ times. This simple fact serves to explain why there are no small warm-blooded animals in the Antarctic or in the ocean and why the largest insect is about as large as the smallest warm-blooded animal. Now, organizations differ widely in size. Does this relationship between surface area and volume tell us anything about organizations?

c. A complex and interesting mathematical theory has been developed to describe the interaction between an animal predator species and its prey (one or more species) in terms of the resultant fluctuations in numbers of the two or more species. It would appear possible to construct an analogy between this situation and that of customers (the predators) and the one or more brands of some product they wish to buy (the prey). Try to define the important factors in the first case and the corresponding factors, if any, in the second.

d. We have previously mentioned some analogies connected with the word "search." Define the important factors involved when an airplane searches for an enemy submarine. Find the analogical factors in a personnel department's search for a salesman.

e. Define the factors which would be important in analyzing an inventory problem. Are there corresponding factors involved in a problem concerning total plant capacity? Are there analogical factors involved in budgeting for a long-range research?

f. A mathematical analysis of a combat between two forces leads to Lanchester's law (see F. W. Lanchester, "Mathematics in Warfare," in J. R. Newman, *The World of Mathematics*, Vol. 4, New York: Simon & Schuster, 1956, pp. 2138-2157). Let:

$$N_1 = \text{units of } A\text{'s force}$$
$$N_2 = \text{units of } B\text{'s force}$$
$$\alpha = \text{hitting power per unit of } A$$
$$\beta = \text{hitting power per unit of } B$$

Then by Lanchester's law the forces are equal when

$$\alpha N_1{}^2 = \beta N_2{}^2.$$

This means that the strength of a force is directly proportional to hitting power per unit and to the square of the number of units. What applicability does this result have to advertising?

g. A complex mathematical theory has been developed to describe the spread of contagious diseases or epidemics through a host population. The spread of the disease depends on such factors as the number of contacts with infected individuals, the probability of contagion through contact, the length of the period of contagion, immunity characteristics, etc. Can you find analogous characteristics in the spread of word of mouth advertising for a product? Might this mathematical theory be useful in advertising?

2. A toy manufacturer has pricing points as follows: $0.09, $0.19, $0.22, $0.29, $0.34, $0.39, $0.62, $0.74, $0.99, $1.19, $1.59. A product is being marketed for which the relationship of sales volume and sales price is known

$$n = 2500 - 2000s \qquad (1.0)$$

where n = sales volume per month, and
  s = sales price (in dollars) per unit.
The cost and profit functions are also known:

$$c = \frac{450}{n} \qquad (1.1)$$

$$p = n(s - c) \qquad (1.2)$$

where c = cost per unit, and
  p = total profit per month.
If the manufacturer holds to his pricing points, how many of his price strategies are profitable? What is his optimum price strategy? Construct the payoff matrix and fill in the values. Assume that dollar profit is the appropriate measure of utility.

Note: If Equations (1.0) and (1.1) are solved simultaneously, and s is set equal to c, the range of profitable sales prices can be determined. When $s = c$, profit must be zero.

Equation (1.2) can be written entirely in terms of s and p. By methods of calculus, the derivative of this equation when set equal to zero can be solved directly for the s value that yields optimum profit.

This example aims to illustrate how mathematical representation can include a great number of strategies with economy. At the same time, it derives outcomes for the gamut of possible strategies and states of nature. Lastly, the mathematical form provides a means for applying the decision criterion to the entire range of possible payoffs and discovering the optimum value. What decision criterion has been applied? Why is it correct for this case?

3. In a well-known case a drug manufacturer overlooked an important state of nature. The result was very tragic. Explain what might have happened, how this was possible, and what might have been done to avoid it.

4. Assume that you can conduct experiments at the rate of one per hour. There are 100 temperature gradients that must be tested against 50 different bimetallic strips for a new thermostat. If individual experiments are to be conducted for each possible circumstance, how much time must be allocated to complete the series? How might a mathematical model be used to advantage?

7 | When Is a Problem Worth Solving?

Granted the general usefulness of operations research, management science and other logical, systematic and quantitative methods of approaching decision problems, it still does not follow that the manager should focus them upon every aspect of his organization. When, then, should he?

WHAT IS A PROBLEM?

We have no intention of trying to completely define what a problem is. The depth of that question is too great for us to attempt to sound it. We shall be content to mention only those few aspects of this question which appear to be most relevant for our discussion.

There is considerable agreement among people on some of the *general characteristics* of problems. Very often the existence and nature of a problem can be diagnosed by means of some obvious questions. Why should this activity be done? Why should it be done in that way? How else can this be done? How should this be done? When should this be done? Who should do this? These questions, and others like them, are *problem-pointers*. The act of questioning indicates the *possible existence* of a problem. By no means does it demonstrate the *real existence* of a problem. We usually use the word *problem* when someone is endeavoring to come to grips with one or more of these questions. To find suitable answers is to *solve the problem*. Generally, we recognize that the same questions can be asked simply from "idle curiosity," and we reserve the word *problem* for cases of "busy curiosity."

Frequently we refer to problems when the person involved is not aware there is any problem at all. For example, most businessmen would maintain that the president of a company that was steadily losing its share of the market had a problem. And they would maintain this even though the president might not know that the problem existed because a rising total market gave his company increasing sales. Of course, they would wonder how he could not know it—but that, for us, is another kind of organizational problem. Similarly, most accountants would hold that a small restaurant owner had a problem if the ratio of his liquid assets to his current liabilities was less than 10 per cent—even if the restaurant owner had never heard of this particular ratio. Any legitimate use of *problem* requires that *somebody must recognize* the problem, even if he is not the person involved. Perhaps we can say that this use of *problem* implies that the person involved *should* be coming to grips with it. One cannot come to grips with a problem until he is aware of its existence. The awareness of a problem is the first prerequisite to dealing with it.

How does one become aware of a problem? There are obviously a multitude of ways, and we do not propose to catalogue them all. But it will be worth mentioning a few of the more common ways.

HEAD-ON CONFRONTATION

First, sometimes we become aware of a problem because reality is so obstreperous that it literally hits us head-on with the problem and there is no conceivable way that we could avoid being aware of it. Examples of this kind of awareness are, unfortunately, particularly numerous. Consider national problems. Only the erosion of millions of acres of farmland leads to an awareness of the problem of soil conservation. Or, the devastation of a hurricane is required before we become aware of the problem of an adequate storm-warning system. Horrifying mid-air collisions produce an awareness of the need for total systems control of aircraft.

There are also many business examples. The manager who becomes aware of the problem posed by a new competitive product because his sales slump to the vanishing point is one case. But we do not mean to imply that all such problems are so catastrophic in their effects. An administrator might not become aware of the problems attendant upon an increasing size of organization until he is in the middle of them, but the effect of the administrator's obtuseness may only be unnecessary inefficiency and wastage. When the consequences are serious, however, becoming aware of a problem in this "head-on" way can be extremely costly. The attempts to cope with the problem must be on an emergency basis and there is no time for careful analysis. Such a situation can only result in a heightening of all the difficulties that surround the efforts to solve a problem even in calmer circumstances.

PRECAUTIONARY MONITORING

Second, some kinds of problems are highlighted by our way of looking at reality. With forethought we are always watching for certain signs. We have called our way of looking at reality "models" of reality. We are now saying that our models of reality generally put some kinds of problems into bold relief. An outstanding example is the administrator's accounting model of his organization. The accounting model is designed to quickly call the administrator's attention to problems signaled by unbalanced cash flow, decreased demand, unit cost increases, higher inventory investments, and a host of similar problems.

This problem-pointing characteristic of models deserves to be emphasized. The layman can be hard put to distinguish between costs and expenses. As a result he is unlikely to notice (become aware of) many problems which anyone familiar with the accounting model would be watching for. But there is a converse to this advantage of models which also deserves emphasis. This is that too great use of any one model is likely to lead to that philosophical error we called *hypostatization*—the confusion of our model with reality. A microscope is an excellent device for looking at bacteria, but useless for seeing stars. A telescope is fine for the stars but not suitable for seeing bacteria. And neither is it any good for reading books. For adequately seeing the universe we need all three: microscopes, telescopes, and good vision. A person endowed with only microscopic vision would have a rather low survival index. It is even difficult to speculate on how his distorted picture of the universe would affect his behavior.

Our models can function as blinders instead of aids to better vision. By giving the illusion of a "total" early-warning system, when in fact it is only "partial," a great disservice may be done. Susceptibility to such illusions is one of the greatest ills that human minds are heir to. Classical economic theory is a good example. The classical economists had a model of the economic activities of society which included only marketplace phenomena. They were so delighted with this model that they resolutely refused to admit the relevance to economics of social problems that were a direct consequence of economic policies. The indefatigable persistence with which some of the classical economists adhered to this position can only be marveled at. Fortunately, the labor of subsequent economists has resulted in economic models that more adequately reflect reality.

In the business world the same kind of thing can happen. Let us consider the accounting model in this regard. Inventory carrying charges are reasonably accessible. There is, however, no entry for profit lost because of unfilled orders, nor is there an entry for the loss of customer goodwill because of out-of-stocks. All kinds of direct costs are emphasized, but there is no place for opportunity costs. Such examples can be multiplied easily. We are not criticizing the accounting model for omitting something it was never intended to do. Rather, we want to point out that an executive who leaned too exclusively on this one model would miss problems that he should be aware of. What would happen? His organization would continue along its path until reality brought him to a sharp realization of the problems—our first method of generating awareness. At that time it might be too late for satisfactory remedial action. The executive must always remember that all models should serve as problem-pointers not as problem-blinders.

EXTERNAL PERTURBATION

Third, awareness of a problem can result from the fact that someone whose role is external to the immediate system discovers its existence. Frequently, this effect is described as "not being able to see the wood for the trees." It also explains why consultants have increasingly participated in organizational affairs. In any case, the "outsider" becomes aware of the problem and presents his discovery with such irresistible logic that others become aware through his efforts. Such contributions to our perception of problems frequently reflect creative genius of a high order. As an example, we can cite Frederick W. Taylor's discovery of the "real" problems of production. The success with which he promulgated his concepts is recorded history. Perhaps it boils down to a question of converting "idle curiosity" into "busy curiosity"—changing problem-pointing questions into real problems that can be studied and solved. In such conversion the government occasionally takes a hand by means of legislation. Thus, a state may make employer contributions to unemployment insurance depend on the amount of use of the insurance by the employees. This is a pointed, and effective, way of making the employer treat the variability in his employment as a problem, rather than simply considering it to be an unfortunate accident of his line of business.

RANDOM SEARCHING

Fourth, and last, one can become so problem-oriented that when no problems can be discovered by any other means one goes looking for them. Such a search is usually predicated on the proposition that "things can't be perfect." Few organizations are without some *problem-finding* group (it may be called a methods department or a value analysis group). Emphasis can be placed on efficiency experts, trouble shooters or systems analysts—whatever the name—to stress preventive treatment; problem-spotting and problem diagnosis are ubiquitous. History provides ample evidence that functions such as these have a significant role to play. Nevertheless, the basis for "looking-for-trouble" is not without its own liabilities. The belief that organized searching will uncover real problems is, in the case of many organizations, only too often justified by the fact that *the searching process creates its own problems.* Such self-justifying processes provide continual reasons for their own existence without necessarily contributing to the organizational well-being. A number of subsequent remarks will be relevant to the question of when one can reasonably initiate a search for problems.

These are some of the major ways in which one can become aware of problems. But it is obvious that not all persons view the same things as problems even when they are faced with the same kinds of situations. Some persons will come to grips with the issues and attempt to resolve them. Others will ignore or defer the issues, i.e., they will not make any effort to solve the problem. For them there is only a problem-pointing question, not a real problem in our sense of the word. Let us consider the reasons for this difference.

PROBLEMS AND OBJECTIVES

We shall treat a particular kind of situation. In one form or another, it arises in a variety of circumstances. Some examples are: a bank manager observes the formation of long waiting lines in front of the open teller windows; the manager of a government tax office observes long waiting lines of citizens desiring assistance in preparing their tax statements; a doctor observes his waiting room filled with prospective patients.

The reactions of the three observers of this phenomenon are likely to be quite different. The bank manager will probably order additional windows to be opened, if any are available. If there are none available and the situation is repeated, he will come to recognize it as a problem and treat it as such. In this event he will consider such strategies as re-designing the bank to get more teller windows, expanding, opening a branch office, or relocating. In short, he will treat this situation as a genuine decision problem and take suitable action to resolve it.

The manager of the tax office is less likely to view the same type of situation as a problem. He will certainly take any available steps equivalent to opening additional teller windows, but he is not oriented to view repetition of the situation as an indication of a problem with which he must deal. Instead, he might view the queues as legitimate punishment for the dilatory citizens who waited till the last minute to fill out their forms. And the citizens themselves probably accept it as such.

The doctor will not have the equivalent of additional windows to open. He is unlikely to view the situation as a problem at all. On the contrary, in his system the waiting line is not undesirable. He can reason that the overcrowded waiting-room is proof to every patient (and other doctors) that he is sought after because he is a good doctor. This is merely confirmation of the patient's choice.

From the standpoint of queuing theory we can say that the doctor and the manager of the tax office are placing high values on their own time and low value on the time of the people waiting. The bank manager, however, puts a higher value on the time of his customers. Why the difference? Why doesn't the bank manager use the same arguments as the other two? Like the manager of the tax office he could say that waiting lines are a form of punishment for customers who insist on coming to the bank from 12:00 to 1:00. If they would distribute themselves more evenly over the whole day they wouldn't have to wait. And like the doctor he could say that the waiting lines prove to his customers that it is a good bank and confirm the wisdom of selecting that bank. But he uses neither of these arguments. Instead, he views the situation as a *problem* to be solved. Why?

The answer to this question is that evidently, the objectives are different in the three cases. There may be other factors as well, but this appears to be the most important reason for the differing responses to the same situation. The doctor will not view the waiting line as a problem. In most cases its absence would be a problem. The doctor's objective is to have a sufficient number of patients, and by his argument the waiting line can contribute to the achievement of his objective. His argument may be wrong but he has considerable *empirical* data which indicate that the waiting line is no impediment to the achievement of his objective. Therefore, he can, and does, ignore it as a problem.

The tax-office manager has a variety of objectives—but they have no reference to the waiting line. One of his objectives is to provide assistance to the taxpayer, but this is in the nature of a free service. If the citizen will not come early and if the citizen wants this free service rather than paying for the advice of a tax consultant, then he must wait. Therefore, the waiting line is not a problem. The objective of the tax-office manager is, so to speak, a reasonable availability of advice for reasonable citizens. There is no objective for "unreasonable" citizens. The bank manager, like the doctor, has an objective of getting the maximum number of customers. He has many competitors who will be delighted to have his customers, and he thinks that long waiting lines are one of the quickest ways to lose customers. Faced with the doctor's argument, he would reply that the patients' payoff is deeply involved in his faith that he has a superb doctor. So the patient will wait, and the waiting line only confirms his evaluation of the quality of the doctor. The bank customer, on the other hand, has no such large payoff from one bank as compared to another. So he will not wait. This is particularly true, since, if anything, waiting is a sign of poor, rather than good bank management. Therefore, the bank manager views waiting lines as impinging directly on his objective and treats the situation as a problem.

This banker's sense of involvement with objectives is an attitude that generally accounts for our selection of the problems with which we try to cope. First and foremost are those problems which have the most direct effect on our objectives. We usually become aware of them first and act on them first. This is natural because we are objective-oriented. The models we find most congenial, and the ones we use the most, are those which help to point out and resolve the problems that have the greatest and the most direct effect on our major objectives. Problems that have a smaller or more indirect effect on our primary objectives are not noticed so quickly. They are not acted upon until priority problems with a more direct or larger effect have been considered.

Now, we are not discussing the question of multiple objectives. Rather, we are considering *problems*. They may have an immediate, direct effect on our objectives or they may have a subsequent and indirect effect. No sharp line of demarcation can be drawn between "indirect" and "smaller." However, by "smaller" effects on our objectives we do not seem to convey all that we mean by "indirect" effects. For example, the entry of a local competitive product in one of our sales regions will have a smaller effect on our objective (maximum sales, maximum profit, and so on) than will the entry of a nationally distributed competitive product in all of our sales regions. But both of these effects are direct ones. On the other hand, an increasing labor turnover in our plant will have a more indirect effect on the objective of maximizing share of the market, although in the long run it could conceivably have a larger effect. This same problem of an increase in labor turnover would have a direct effect on the objective of maximizing profit. A problem relating to financial structure would have an indirect effect on most marketing objectives but a direct effect on the objective of paying a given, or maximum, dividend to stockholders.

As one would expect, the directness or indirectness of the effect of a problem on an objective depends on the objective as well as the problem. The difficulty involved in distinguishing between direct and indirect effects is illustrated by a problem in product quality. A slight decrease in product quality would probably have only an indirect effect on most objectives, but a large decrease would undoubtedly have a direct effect. It is useful to acknowledge that some differences can be defined only in terms of degree.

Let us attempt to define the difference between direct and indirect effects. There is clearly a differentiating element of temporal *immediacy;* the more immediate the more direct. But other characteristics are also involved. These reflect the fact that the awareness of problems increases as they become more related to the objectives. In other words, when objectives are *sensitive* to certain problems—these problems will be noted and acted upon before those with an indirect effect. And, of course, the *size of the effect* must be considered. Problems with a large effect are likely to be observed and acted upon before problems with a relatively smaller effect. With this in mind, why do we observe differences in the procedures that various organizations follow in dealing with problems? This observation remains true even when the problems are similar in type and in their effect on the organization's objectives. Let us consider why this is so.

PROBLEMS AND THE SIZE OF ORGANIZATIONS

The question we have raised above can be typified by an example. Company *A* produces electronic equipment for a *local market*. It is small and profitable. The company has a problem situation in the form of too high a turnover in the plant labor force. Having become aware of the problem, *A*'s plant manager calls a meeting of his foremen and discusses the problem with them for an hour. Finding no answers, he closes the meeting by ordering the installation of a suggestion box. Then he returns hastily to other, more pressing problems. Company *B* produces electronic equipment for the *national market*. It is large and profitable. It, too, has a problem in the form of too high a turnover in the plant labor force. Having become aware of the problem, *B*'s vice-president in charge of production calls in a team of consultants, which includes industrial psychologists, sociologists, and an applied anthropologist. After a reasonably lengthy investigation they will probably make some good recommendations as to how the problem can be resolved. The responses of the two companies to the same problem are totally different.

The kind of situation typified by this example is so common that similar examples are probably familiar to anyone acquainted with organizational realities. Our question is: Why does this difference occur in response to identical problems?

The answer, speaking generally, is that the *returns* that result from solving a problem *tend to be proportional to the size, income, sales, or profit* of the organization, while the *cost* of solving the problem *tends to be a fixed amount*. We want first to justify this answer and then to discuss how it affects organizational attitudes toward problems.

The first part of the answer is that the returns that result from solving a problem tend to be proportional to some measure of the organization's involvement in the area of the problem. Such measures are income, sales, budgets, operating costs, profit, and the like. This requires but little demonstration. An organization with extra labor costs of $100,000 per year owing to high turnover may save $25,000 or $50,000 from cutting the amount of turnover. But they certainly can't save more than $100,000. Another organization with an extra labor cost of $1,000,000 owing to high turnover could easily save more than $100,000 by cutting the amount of turnover. Furthermore, comparable amounts of improvement in the two organizations would probably save comparable percentages of the respective total extra costs. This is what is meant by the statement that returns tend to be proportional to the measure of the organizational involvement in the problem area. The measure of involvement here is the extra cost owing to the high turnover. And lest it be objected that this measure wouldn't be known, let us hasten to add that the same conclusion would follow if total labor costs were used as the measure.

The same kind of argument applies to most kinds of organizational problems. The solution of a marketing problem might increase sales by any reasonable range of amounts, but the increase would generally be proportional to the sales. A company with ten times the annual sales of another company that solved the same problem would probably get around ten times the amount of return in sales units, or about the *same percentage* return. It is exceptions to this statement that demand explanation rather than the statement itself.

The second part of the answer is that the cost of solving a problem tends to be a fixed amount. This requires justification because it is certainly an overgeneralization and is false in some cases. Nonetheless, it is generally a reasonable approximation to the facts. The important word is "tends"—we are not stating an equation. The major reason why the cost of solving a problem tends to be a fixed amount is that the amounts of information and analysis required are more nearly a *function of the problem than they are of the size of the organization* that has the problem.

Consider an analysis of an inventory problem as an example. A small firm may have two or three thousand items in inventory, whereas a large firm may have 200,000. But what will be typically required, in either case, will be a careful analysis of a relatively small selection of items. Once an inventory system has been worked out it will generally be up to the organization's personnel, with a little coaching, to get the system installed on all the items. Much of the time spent in analysis will be used in careful studies of generic problem characteristics as they apply to the special circumstances and needs of the organization. This represents a general cost of the study which will be applicable regardless of the number of items studied. Add to this the fact that a fair amount of the time will be spent in establishing the necessary working relationships and channels of communication. The result is that a large percentage of the cost of solving the inventory problem is fixed, and only a small percentage depends on the number of items. This is the hallmark of an essentially fixed cost, which is exactly our thesis. Similarly, consider the case of a problem involving the allocation of salesmen's time. The fact that one company has ten

times the number of salesmen another company has does not necessarily
make the study of the first company's problem more expensive. The
study of customer characteristics will be required in either case and
the same mathematical models will be tried in both cases. The fixed
costs, in short, are high. A great number of organizational problems
are of this sort.

There are, of course, problems for which the cost of a solution is
directly proportional to the size of the organization. An outstanding
example of this kind of problem is one in the area of information flow.
These are the problems that prompt systems analysis in the hope of
improvement by redesign of the organization's communication network. The communication network consists of links between various
processors of information. If all possible links existed (between every
pair of information-processors) the number of links would increase
in proportion to the square of the number of information-processors.
Generally this isn't the case, but the number of links certainly increases
as fast as the number of information-processors. The work, and hence
cost, of an analysis of such a system depends on the number of such
links. Therefore, a large organization, having more information-processors and more links, can expect a systems study to cost more money
than it would for a small organization. Despite exceptions, it appears
that the majority of problems are such that their *solutions involve
high fixed costs.*

What does this imply in terms of company attitudes to problems?
The main consideration involves company size. Let's take a problem
in marketing for which a solution would involve a 2 per cent increase
in sales for one year. In accord with our argument we will suppose
that a solution will cost $50,000. If we assume a 10 per cent gross profit
on sales, it follows that a company's sales would have to be at least
$25,000,000 per year—since ($25,000,000) (0.02) (0.1) = $50,000—be-
fore it would be profitable to undertake the study. Smaller companies
would be equally delighted to gain 2 per cent of their sales by solving
the given problem, but it is simply not economical for them to have it
solved. Similarly, in the case of the two manufacturers of electronic
equipment (A and B), with which we commenced this section, equivalent percentage improvements might result if the problem were solved
in the two cases. But the difference in the amount of involvement in
the problem area makes it economical for the larger company to undertake an expensive analysis of the problem, which would be completely
uneconomical for the smaller company.

This argument, then, serves to explain the reason behind the commonly observed difference in organizational responses to problems. Managers can be acting with complete rationality but one will initiate an extensive, and often expensive, search for a solution while another essentially ignores the problem.

Some further ramifications of the same argument are worth discussing. First, we have assumed in the above discussions that the solution to the problem is assured if only the search is undertaken. This, of course, is a very bad assumption. A manager's life would be delightfully easy if he knew that each of his problems could be solved by retaining some suitable consultants or by employing his own specialists. Unfortunately, this is far from true. The manager may invest considerable sums in an attempt to solve a problem and may find no solution at all. In this event he still has his problem plus the realization that he has wasted resources in a vain effort to solve it.

This situation can be described by saying that a search for a problem solution has some probability of being successful. The possibility of making an immediate and realistic estimate of this probability must be questioned. For the present, it will be sufficient to observe that there is some probability of finding a solution, whether we know what it is or not. Now, since there is usually a continual succession of problems in any organization, it follows that a succession of choices must be made. For any problem, one can attempt to find the solution, or else ignore the problem. The situation also might be immediately resolved by utilizing managerial intuition.

At present, let us note that there are two available possibilities: (1) undertake a search for the solution to the problem, which will cost some particular sum and which will have some specified probability of success, or (2) do something else that will not involve expenditures to find the solution (including decision by default) to the problem. These choices are available for each problem and there is a constant succession of problems. So formulated, the situation of an organization regarding its problems bears a striking resemblance to that of a gambler making wagers on some chance device. The problems are the successive wagers and, like the gambler, the managers are not forced to make a bet. The sum required to search for the problem solution is the amount of the wager, and the return that results if the solution is found represents the amount won if the wager is successful. Finally, the probability that a solution will be found is the probability of winning. The analogy is complete and we might expect that probability theory, which has much to say about gambler's chances, might have something to say about the organization's policy regarding its problems, which in fact it does.

In probability theory this problem is treated under the descriptive title, "The Problem of the Gambler's Ruin." The organization that is establishing a policy for dealing with its problems is not a gambler, and it is not often in a position where it is really risking ruin by attempts to solve its problems. However, because of the analogies we have pointed out, it is possible to consider the organization's situation in the light of the results available from an analysis of this intriguing comparison. Rational managers should recognize, and take account of, the fact that the allocation of funds to a search for problem solutions bears a strong *family* resemblance to the problem facing a gambler with a limited capital. This does not mean that managers and administrators need be experts in probability theory. The point is simply that their allocation of problem-solving funds should be weighted in the direction indicated by the theory.[1]

Two points remain to be mentioned in this brief discussion of the effect of an organization's size on the approach to problems. First, most returns from solutions to problems are not lump sums received upon implementation of whatever is indicated by the problem solution. Instead they are in the form of some increment to income over a period of years. Ordinarily the number of years cannot be assumed to be too great because future changes in conditions will either require a new solution or will render the whole problem irrelevant. But, even so, the future income stream must be discounted back to present worth before any conclusions can be drawn concerning the advisability of searching for a solution. From the standpoint of the smaller organization, the effect is to require a greater margin of safety (as compared to the larger one) against the possibility of a bad-luck streak. The spreading of the possible return over a number of years means that there is less chance of one good solution's sustaining the available funds against several failures. This requires a greater relative increase in the safety margin for the smaller organization than it does for the larger one.

Second, as soon as probabilities of gains and losses enter the picture the question of the utility of money arises. The effect of the introduction of the utility of money was illustrated by our discussion of the self-insurance problem earlier. The reader will remember that when due

---

[1] See David W. Miller and Martin K. Starr, *Executive Decisions and Operations Research* (Englewood Cliffs, N.J.: Prentice-Hall, Inc., 1960), pp. 370-74.

account was taken of differing utilities for money the organization with larger resources could assume risks that a smaller one could not. Precisely the same effect results in this case. The introduction of utilities for money will result in the smaller organization's having to forego still more searches for solutions to problems, which the larger enterprise can easily undertake.

The net effect of ruin theory, as well as the other factors that we have considered here, is that there is a strong relationship between an organization's size and the problems which it can attempt to solve. We would not expect to find smaller organizations undertaking the solution of problems that have an indirect or smaller effect on their objectives. Only large organizations can afford to assume the risk of undertaking solutions to problems that have an attenuated, indirect effect on primary objectives.

PROBLEM SOLVING: THE POTENTIAL GAIN

The decision concerning the allocation of funds for problem-solving is, of course, a decision problem, and one that is quite similar to the many others we have discussed throughout the book. One difference, however, is that this decision problem is one that the manager often has to block out for himself. It is not uncommon to have a preliminary analysis performed in order to determine the desirability of undertaking some particularly expensive search for a problem solution, but even in this case the manager must himself reach the first decision: to undertake the preliminary investigation.

Having recognized that this is a decision problem, let us try to identify the usual components of a decision problem. First, what are the strategies? This depends on the kind of problem that has arisen. On the one hand it may be some aspect of an organization's operations that has never previously been considered as a problem. An example might be labor turnover in a small to medium-sized plant. In this case the strategies might consist of (1) continuing to ignore the problem or (2) investing various sums of money in an attempt to solve the problem. On the other hand, there are problems that have always been treated as decision problems but that are now being considered to be perhaps worthy of a more careful analysis. The past method of handling the problem may have been some established policy, or an executive may have decided each case on its merits. In this event, the strategies in the decision problem would include (1) the continuation of the previous procedure and (2) the allocation of various sums of money to the solution of the problem. The states of nature are the various possible situations that may pertain to the problem. The payoff is the return that results for the various combinations of strategies and states of nature. It is the payoff that we will now consider.

Many of the decision problems we have discussed have been a kind in which something positive was definitely going to be done and it was a question of choosing the most profitable or the least costly "something" to do. For example, there will be an ordering policy of some kind in an inventory problem. The relevant decision problem is to choose the least costly one. But in the present decision problem the question is, essentially, whether to invest in a search for a solution or not. Since the required investment will ordinarily be fairly well fixed, it follows that we will never make the search unless it is possible that the return can be larger than the cost of the search. We may not attempt to find the solution even if the return can be larger than the cost, but we certainly won't make the search if the return cannot possibly be larger than the cost. Therefore, a reasonable first step is to raise the question: What is the maximum possible return if this problem is solved?

The answer involves a comparison of how the organization stands with regard to the objective affected by the problem and what the organization might conceivably achieve if it tried. It is clear that the latter is more difficult to estimate than the former. But even knowing how the organization stands with regard to some objectives is quite difficult. Any objective that has a natural quantified measure causes no difficulties. A company's position with respect to profit is simply the amount of percentage of profit it is making. How it stands with regard to labor turnover is some suitable measure of turnover like the percentage of new employees per month. But what the company's position is with regard to labor relations, for example, is hard to define. We have already discussed this problem extensively and we will not repeat our remarks here. In the present context, if the objective cannot be quantified then the approach we are developing here cannot be used. We intend to find some measure of the distance separating the actual position of the company from its conceivable position. Distance implies measurement and if the objective cannot be quantified we cannot measure the distance. Therefore, we will assume that the objective in question has a quantitative measure and that the company's actual position with regard to the objective can be determined.

The more difficult part of the question is that dealing with what the company might conceivably achieve. There are two major ways (three if we include executive experience and intuition) by which the best conceivable position of the company with regard to the objective might be determined. An analogy from a different field suggests the first method. An engineer who designs steam engines is interested in measuring their efficiency. He can do this very easily because the basic laws of thermo-dynamics imply a top efficiency beyond which no engine can possibly go. This, then, represents a theoretical maximum for any steam engine. Are there any such theoretical maxima for organizations? If there are any, then these would supply an upper (or lower) limit to the con-ceivable position of the company.

The answer is that there are such absolute maxima for organizations as well as for steam engines. As a matter of fact, there are quite a large number of them. Some of them are tritely obvious but others are far from trite or obvious. Obvious ones come from areas where achievement can be measured in percentages of some total amount. Ob-viously, in this case, a percentage cannot be bigger than 100 per cent nor smaller than 0 per cent. For example, labor turnover, readers of a magazine who notice an advertisement, potential customers reached by an advertising campaign, percentage defectives in production, and many similar kinds of measures have theoretical maxima or minima of 100 per cent or 0 per cent.

Many times, there is no such theoretical limit and it is necessary to try the second method: use data that show the positions of other or-ganizations with regard to the objective in question. The maximum or minimum obtained in practice can be used as an approximation to the limit. Such data are often available from trade associations; some-times they appear in annual reports, or they may be found in special studies. The more similar the other organizations, the more reliable the extrapolation, but for many objectives it is possible to establish empirical limits on the basis of data from quite dissimilar organiza-tions. For such measures as inventory turnover, sales per dollar of ad-vertising, labor turnover, and many measures of rates of return it is usually possible to determine practical upper and lower limits in this manner.

Finally, of course, if no other limit can be obtained the manager can use his own experience as a guide to estimating the limit of possible improvement. It is important to have some kind of estimated limit be-cause of the obvious, but sometimes overlooked, fact that no search for a solution should be undertaken unless it is at least possible to gain a return from the solution that exceeds the cost of the search. Once a limit has been established, the distance separating the actual position from the limit gives the maximum possible improvement as a result of solving the problem. Of course, the problem may not be solved, and even if it is solved the actual improvement will probably fall far short of the maximum possible improvement. But the knowledge of the upper bound that exists to the return from a solution is, nonetheless, a necessary component of this decision problem. When the upper limit has been determined, it is then necessary to estimate the actual returns that may be achieved. We now proceed to a discussion of this difficult question.

WHAT IS A PROBLEM SOLUTION WORTH?

This question is obviously a complex one. But it is equally obvious that it is the key to a rational analysis of the decision problem of whether or not to undertake a search for a solution. The main difficulty results from the large variety of ways in which the manager might profit from a search for a solution. Let us list some of them.

1. He may profit from the mere fact of a search for a solution even if no solution is found. For example, a study of productive efficiency sometimes results in greater efficiency purely because of the response of the personnel to the fact that their efficiency is being studied.
2. He may profit from a search that doesn't find a solution by discovering that some factor that he had been considering important is not so important. As a result, he will no longer have to worry about that factor. For example, a company that undertakes a study to minimize direct-mail duplication may not discover the solution, but as a result of the investigation it may learn that duplication is not large enough to warrant further attention.
3. He may profit because the range of the possible states of nature is narrowed. Any successful search for improved predicting methods is an example.
4. He may profit because the number of strategies that he needs to consider is decreased. Often this results because the complex system involved in the problem is found to depend on some key component. Only those strategies which affect this key part need be considered.
5. He may profit by discovering a more suitable measure of effectiveness.
6. He may profit by obtaining good estimates of the probabilities of

the states of nature. An example would be that of a company considering a sizable expansion in a foreign country. Such a company might undertake a study to ascertain the probabilities of war, revolution, socialization, and other relevant states of nature.

7. He may profit by discovering the correct evaluation of the payoff measure. As an example we can cite studies made of the optimal allocation of salesmen's time in which it has been found that the payoff measure (sales, for example) is related to the allocation of time in ways that are far from obvious.

Still other kinds of returns from solutions could be given. But it is not worthwhile to try listing all of them, even assuming that this could be done. We cannot discuss every possible gain that might be derived from a search for a solution. The important thing to note is that the process of searching for a solution can produce peripheral benefits that help to justify the decision to solve the problem. In other cases, the side effects may not be beneficial. This occurs, in particular, when an efficient process must be disturbed to collect information necessary for the solution of the problem. The decision-maker must consider the pros and cons of the side effects that might result from the decision to solve a problem.

Basically, the value of a solution can be treated in much the same way as any other value problem. We can distinguish at least three different types of value situations. In the first place, we have the situation in which the solution to a problem has a value determined by the supply and demand for solutions. For example, the demand for oil and the frequency with which varying quantities of oil are found permit us to specify the value of this solution. Similarly, the value of the solution to the problem of finding an adequate number of engineers depends upon the supply of engineers and the company's demand for them. The second type of value situation is the one in which there is an imputed value for the solution that is independent of the supply and demand for such solutions. For example, when an air-sea rescue operation is undertaken to locate a pilot downed at sea, the combined cost of all of the equipment and personnel employed in the search provides at least a lower bound for the imputed value of the pilot's life. In business, imputed values must be used when a numerical equivalent cannot be found. This is the case for employee morale, company goodwill, community relations, and so forth. The third type of value situation we will mention is one in which the value of the solution is basically a measure of improved efficiency. As we have previously stated, it is sometimes possible to estimate an upper limit for efficiency, in which case, if the organization knows its present efficiency it is able to estimate the probable value of a solution. The estimate depends upon the anticipated effectiveness of the strategies (techniques) that will be employed. Consequently, the appraisal of techniques is of great importance in the estimation of the value of a solution. With standard techniques and methods, and an evaluation of the data that are used, it is possible to estimate the degree to which the best possible result will be approximated. With nonstandard techniques, it is necessary to approach this problem in stages. At each stage, the previous results and additional information gained can be used to reestimate the probable value of the solution that will result if the problem-solving procedure is continued.

It is not unusual for the solution of one problem to bring to light the value to be gained from solving another problem. However, many problems are not involved in such mutual relationships, and it is necessary to find still other means for estimating the worth of a solution.

The general procedure we would like to be able to follow is clear. We must attempt to estimate the payoffs that result from solutions. Since we will often have an estimate of the maximum possible improvement that could result, it may be most convenient to express the different payoffs as percentages of this maximum. Then, by determining the effect of a percentage-point improvement on some convenient dollar measurement (sales, costs, profit, and the like), it will be possible to convert the payoff measures to dollars, which can be included directly with the dollar cost of the search in evaluating the expected returns of the strategies. This, of course, is far easier said than done, but it is quite straightforward for many problems. In estimating the payoffs it is often possible to utilize published studies showing the improvements that resulted from similar searches for solutions. In this context it may be noted that the smaller organization has an advantage here. In accordance with our previous argument it is likely that the smaller organization will be dealing with problems that have a direct and large effect on its primary objectives. These are the problems which have most often been handled by other organizations and, hence, for which the greatest amount of information on resulting improvements is available. The larger organization may be dealing with a specialized problem that has never, or rarely, been dealt with before. This makes it more unlikely that any significant amount of information concerning improvements will be available.

One rule of thumb is worth noting in connection with the fact that some problems have always been recognized as being decision problems (although no formal search has been made to find a solution); others have not been considered to be decision problems. The first kind of problem will have had the attention of a decision-maker. If he has had the benefit of an accurate measure of the payoff from his decisions he will have had the opportunity to develop his own methods for approaching an optimal selection of strategy. Under usual conditions he will have done so—and with a fair degree of success if the problem is not exceedingly complex. Thus, a solution for a problem of this kind is not likely to produce nearly so much improvement as will a solution to the other kind of problem.

To illustrate the difference we will contrast three problems. First, consider a transportation problem involving factories and warehouses. Here the costs are given and the total cost of any shipping strategy is immediately available. Any conscientious manager would approach the minimum-cost strategy for this problem, over a period of time, even for a large number of factories and warehouses. Second, consider an inventory problem. Here the manager will rarely receive the information necessary to completely evaluate his own decisions. He will not, therefore, be so likely to improve his decisions beyond a certain point— even with practice. Third, consider a problem in plant location that has never arisen before. Clearly, there is no basis for improving performance on a unique problem. Generally speaking the relative improvements resulting from solutions will be smaller in the first case, larger in the second, and largest in the third. We must emphasize the word "relative." It means the improvement as a percentage of the cost of the decision-maker's unaided decision. We cannot say anything about the absolute improvements because this measure depends on the specific circumstances of the problems. The moral is simple: Never underestimate the ability of the manager to approach the optimal strategy *if* he is given an adequate feedback of information.

In the attempt to evaluate the return from a solution, one of the greatest difficulties results from the fact that a solution may be found but the determining factors may be outside the manager's control. This would essentially eliminate the possibility of a return from the solution. For example, the labor-turnover problem might be analyzed at considerable expense only to find that the main contributing factors were sociological conditions over which the organization had no control. There is no certain way of handling this difficulty, but it is possible in many cases to estimate the hazard. Usually the manager has reasonable knowledge of the factors that he controls. This being so, he may be able to discover, either from his own organization's experience or from that of similar ones:

1. That the quantitative measure of his objective in the past has varied, while the factors under his control remained essentially constant,

   or

2. That the quantitative measure of his objective in the past has remained fairly constant, while the factors under his control varied.

In either case, one can assume that the factors under his control are not sufficient to determine the objective measure (payoff). Hence, there is a good chance a solution will disclose that the important factors in determining his payoff are outside his control. However, it is known that feedback systems can produce variation although a constant strategy is being maintained. In this case, the lack of sufficient information about the system could mislead the decision-maker into believing that he has no control over the situation, when in fact he does have control but he doesn't know how it works.

Similarly, there is a problem with respect to the second point. The quantitative measure of the objective may remain constant while the control factors are varied, but the time lag may be so great that the effect of varying the controls cannot be observed. For example, changing advertising effort may not affect short-term sales but profoundly affect long-term sales. Consequently, the manager must evaluate the kind of situation that prevails when he attempts to determine how much control he exercises in obtaining a solution.

Whenever a situation arises in which the decision-maker appears to have no strategy available that will permit him to utilize the results of a solution, the value of that solution would be nil. For example, the fact that a company knows who its potential customers are will be of limited value unless specific means are available for reaching these customers. If no medium exists that includes a larger proportion of potential customers in its audience than exists in the general population, the characterization of potential customers is valueless—at least for selecting optimal media. Sometimes persistence and imagination can succeed in devising a strategy that will give value to a solution. This depends on the caliber of the men who attempt to resolve the problem. It is not our intention to discuss such questions as the kind of men needed to provide creative and resourceful ideas with respect to the utilization of solutions. Still, the value of a solution will frequently increase because an ingenious way has been found for putting the result to work.

One additional factor should be mentioned that affects the value of a solution. Competitive incentives exist that are difficult to evaluate. Many times a value must be imputed for being the first to achieve something. Frequently, a company that is second benefits at the expense of the first. In many other cases, the advantage of being first gives the company that pioneers the solution a lead that cannot be overcome. The position of a company with respect to its competitors and the characteristics of the market must, therefore, be considered when attempts are made to place a value on a solution.

We can see that the value of a solution is a function of many factors. If it can be represented on a single scale, such as dollars, then a direct decision can be made between possible alternative problems to be studied. If it is not possible to estimate the value of a solution on a single scale, then it is necessary to use the methods that we have discussed for comparing outcomes in terms of the multiple objectives of the organization.

PROBLEMS

1. How does the right to obtain a patent affect the value of a company being first with a solution? Discuss.

2. Why do many large companies follow very liberal policies with respect to granting other companies the right to use the patents which they hold? Discuss.

3. What advantages and disadvantages are there in letting a competitor have a large research budget while your company puts equivalent sums into advertising? Discuss.

4. Based on the effects of problem-solving on large and small organizations, what arguments pro and con can be developed for federal, state, or municipal government being responsible for:

   a. Pollution control?
   b. Medical research?
   c. Urban development?
   d. Transportation and communication regulation?
   e. Outerspace systems?

Now examine the same problem areas with respect to private industry, university participation, or private foundation operations.

5. How do small and large system considerations affect military research?

6. a. All of the hospitals in a large metropolitan area are overcrowded. Is this a problem? Discuss in rational terms.
   b. Is overpopulation a problem in all parts of the world? Discuss.
   c. Why is it that in the 1950s the pollution problem did not exist?

7. You are involved in seeking a site for a jet airport to service a large metropolitan center. Lay out the nature of the problem you face.

8. A severe water shortage is alleviated in a certain region of the country when Nature brings a long-standing drought to an end. As a result, all emergency procedures are canceled. What happened to the problem that existed before the rains came? [1]

9. What problems are brought to mind by the concept of desalinization?

10. How is problem-solving related to roulette?

11. Suppose you are responsible for the advertising and promotion of a very expensive imported champagne. How would you assess the potential worth of a large-scale market study that undertakes to define your potential customers?

12. Suppose you must decide whether to accept or reject a lot of 100 expensive electrical components for use in our space exploration program. You can sample the lot, but each item sampled is destroyed by the test. Explain your analysis of this situation in order to decide how to proceed.

[1] During the shortage it was maintained that more reservoirs were needed. To this suggestion someone responded "Why do we need more reservoirs? The ones we have aren't full?" Comment on this argument.

Bibliography

Ashby, W. Ross, *An Introduction to Cybernetics.* New York: John Wiley & Sons, Inc., 1956.

Baumol, William J., *Economic Theory and Operations Analysis* (2nd ed.). Englewood Cliffs, N.J.: Prentice-Hall, Inc., 1966.

Beer, Stafford, *Cybernetics and Management.* New York: John Wiley & Sons, Inc., 1959.

Bross, Irwin D. J., *Design for Decision.* New York: The Macmillan Company, 1953.

Campbell, Norman R., *Foundations of Science.* New York: Dover Publications, Inc., 1957.

Cherry, Colin, *On Human Communications.* Cambridge, Mass.: The Technology Press of Massachusetts Institute of Technology, 1957.

Churchman, C. West, *Prediction and Optimal Decision.* Englewood Cliffs, N.J.: Prentice-Hall, Inc., 1961.

———, *Theory of Experimental Inference.* New York: The Macmillan Company, 1950.

de Latil, Pierre (tran. Y. M. Golla), *Thinking by Machine, A Study of Cybernetics.* Boston, Mass.: Houghton Mifflin Co., 1957.

Dorfman, Robert (ed.), *Measuring Benefits of Government Investments.* Washington, D.C.: The Brookings Institution, 1965.

Forrester, J. W., *Industrial Dynamics,* New York: John Wiley & Sons, Inc., 1961.

Good, I. J., *Probability and the Weighing of Evidence.* London: Griffin, 1950.

Gregory, R. H., and R. L. Van Horn, *Automatic Data-Processing Systems.* Belmont, Calif.: Wadsworth Publishing Co., Inc., 1962.

Hall, Arthur D., *A Methodology for Systems Engineering.* Princeton, N.J.: D. Van Nostrand Co., Inc., 1962.

Hare, Van Court, Jr., *Systems Analysis, A Diagnostic Approach.* New York: Harcourt, Brace & World, Inc., 1967.

Kemeny, J. G., J. L. Snell, and G. L. Thompson, *Introduction to Finite Mathematics* (2nd ed.). Englewood Cliffs, N.J.: Prentice-Hall, Inc., 1957.

Luce, R. Duncan, and Howard Raiffa, *Games and Decisions.* New York: John Wiley & Sons, Inc., 1958.

March, James G. and Herbert A. Simon, *Organizations.* New York: John Wiley & Sons, Inc., 1958.

McCloskey, J. F. and F. N. Trefethen (eds.), *Operations Research for Management,* Volume I. Baltimore, Md.: Johns Hopkins Press, 1954.

McCloskey, J. F. and J. M. Coppinger (eds.), *Operations Research for Management,* Volume 2. Baltimore, Md.: Johns Hopkins Press, 1956.

McDonald, John, *Strategy in Poker, Business and War.* New York: W. W. Norton & Company, Inc., 1950.

McKean, Roland N., *Efficiency in Government through Systems Analysis.* New York: John Wiley & Sons, Inc., 1958.

McPhee, William N., *Formal Theories of Mass Behavior.* New York: Free Press of Glencoe, 1963.

Orcutt, G. H., M. Greenburger, and A. M. Rivlin, *Decision-Unit Models and Simulation of the United States Economy.* New York: Harper & Row, Publishers, 1959.

Postley, John A., *Computers and People.* New York: McGraw-Hill Book Company, 1960.

Sasieni, M., A. Yaspan, and L. Friedman, *Operations Research, Methods and Problems.* New York: John Wiley & Sons, Inc., 1959.

Shelly, Maynard W. II, and Glenn L. Ryan (eds.), *Human Judgments and Optimality.* New York: John Wiley & Sons, Inc., 1964.

Simon, Herbert A., *Models of Man.* New York: John Wiley & Sons, Inc., 1957.

Simon, H. A., *The New Science of Management Decisions.* New York: Harper & Row, Publishers, 1960.

Siu, R. G. H., *The Tao of Science.* New York: John Wiley & Sons, Inc., 1957.

Torgerson, Warren S., *Theory and Methods of Scaling.* New York: John Wiley & Sons, Inc., 1958.

Wasserman, Paul, with Fred S. Silander, *Decision-Making, an Annotated Bibliography.* Ithaca, N.Y.: Cornell University, Graduate School of Business and Public Administration, 1958. Also see their supplements.

Whyte, William H., Jr., *The Organization Man.* New York: Simon & Schuster, Inc., 1956.

Williams, J. D., *The Compleat Strategyst.* New York: McGraw-Hill Book Company, 1954.

Index